Know Your Numbers

Circle or write the correct answers.

1. Which number is forty-one thousand five hundred thirty-six?

   a. 41,563   b. 401,536   c. 41,036   d. 41,536

2. Write the word form of the numerals.

   1,683 ____________________

   21,379 ____________________

3. Write the expanded form of the numerals.

   749 ____________________

   9,681 ____________________

   309 ____________________

   7,439 ____________________

4. Read the expanded form, then write the standard form of the numeral.

   800 + 60 + 7 ____________________

   4,000 + 200 + 70 + 3 ____________________

   400 + 60 + 7 ____________________

5. Circle the thousands place in the numerals.

   3,489   79,473   19,341   473,618

6. Circle the ten thousands place in the numerals.

   475,614   1,649,541   817,683   5,649,196

7. Circle the hundreds place in the numerals.

   1,443,623   16,945   7,485   516,689

Show What You Know

1. Round the following numerals to the nearest ten.

43 ________ 17 ________ 61 ________ 85 ________

2. Round the following addition and subtraction sentences to the nearest ten, then perform the operation.

46 + 18 = + ____	38 + 27 = + ____	22 + 73 = + ____	51 + 12 = + ____	87 + 69 = + ____
74 − 48 = − ____	57 − 29 = − ____	92 − 43 = − ____	39 − 9 = − ____	64 − 38 = − ____

3. Write the addition and subtraction fact families for each set.

(7, 12, 5) ________________
(14, 8, 6) ________________
(8, 7, 15) ________________
(9, 4, 13) ________________
(16, 8, 8) ________________
(9, 17, 8) ________________

4. Write the multiplication and division fact families for each set.

(7, 6, 42) ________________
(32, 8, 4) ________________
(7, 8, 56) ________________
(9, 4, 36) ________________
(3, 8, 24) ________________
(5, 4, 20) ________________

5. Write the inverse operation for each number sentence.

6 x 5 = 30 ____	7 x 3 = 21 ____	8 ÷ 2 = 4 ____	18 ÷ 9 = 2 ____
56 ÷ 8 = 7 ____	6 x 9 = 54 ____	36 ÷ 6 = 6 ____	6 x 4 = 24 ____
9 + 4 = 13 ____	5 + 6 = 11 ____	8 + 5 = 13 ____	17 − 9 = 8 ____
14 − 7 = 7 ____	15 − 8 = 7 ____	5 + 9 = 14 ____	5 + 5 = 10 ____

Stretch Your Number Sense

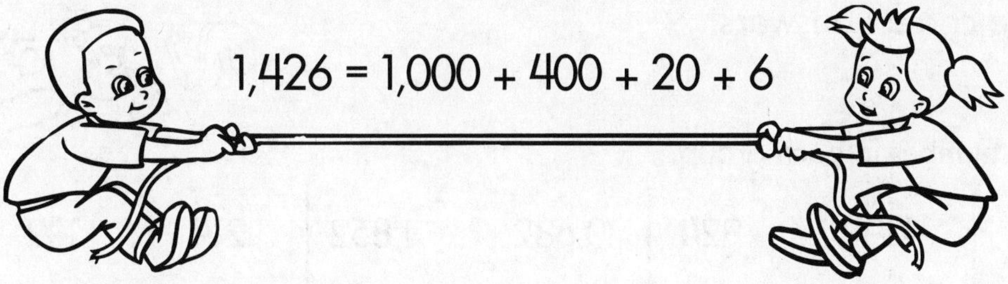

Rewrite each numeral in expanded form.

4,378 ______________________________

6,743 ______________________________

18,734 ______________________________

754,219 ______________________________

Write the numerals in word form.

Example: 7,436 = seven thousand, four hundred thirty-six

9,408 ______________________________

24,972 ______________________________

17,987 ______________________________

64,805 ______________________________

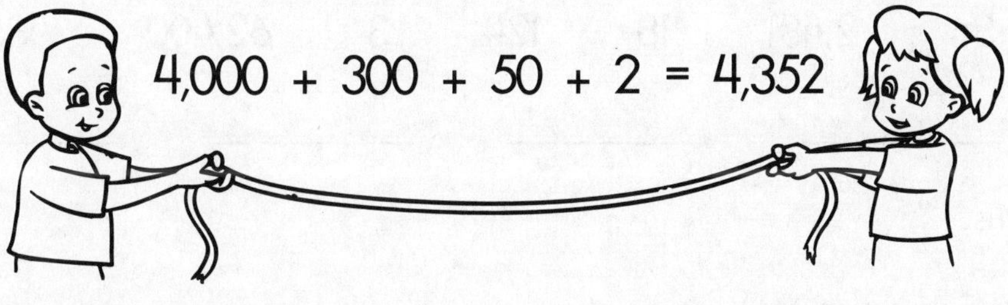

Read the expanded form of the numeral, then write the numeral in standard form.

10,000 + 7,000 + 500 + 30 + 2 = ____________________

6,000 + 200 + 40 + 1 = ____________________

30,000 + 1,000 + 800 + 60 + 5 = ____________________

7,000 + 400 + 80 + 3 = ____________________

80,000 + 700 + 40 + 9 = ____________________

Numbers Popping Up Everywhere!

Circle or write the correct answers.

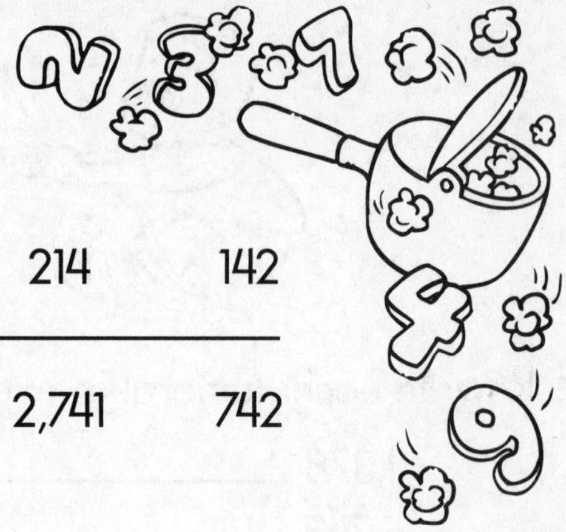

1. Circle the greater number in each group.

3,281	328	429	924	10,582	1,852	214	142
16,927	19,672	752	5,217	3,863	3,683	2,741	742

2. Rewrite the following numbers in order from **greatest** to **least**.

6,791 721 1,403 614 21,572 206

Greatest ________ ________ ________ ________ ________ ________ Least

3. Make eight different numbers using the digits 7,4,1 and 8.
Write the numbers in order from **greatest** to **least**.

Greatest 8,741 ________ ________ ________ ________ ________ ________ ________ Least

4. Circle the **odd** numbers. Write the **even** numbers below.

27 462 86 2,481 18 124 3 62,400 483 211

________ ________ ________ ________ ________

5. Continue the patterns.

sixty-three, sixty-five, sixty-seven, ________________, ________________

2,779 2,782 2,785 2,788 ________, ________, ________

5 8 11 14 17 ________, ________, ________

16 24 32 40 ________, ________, ________

Coach's Helper

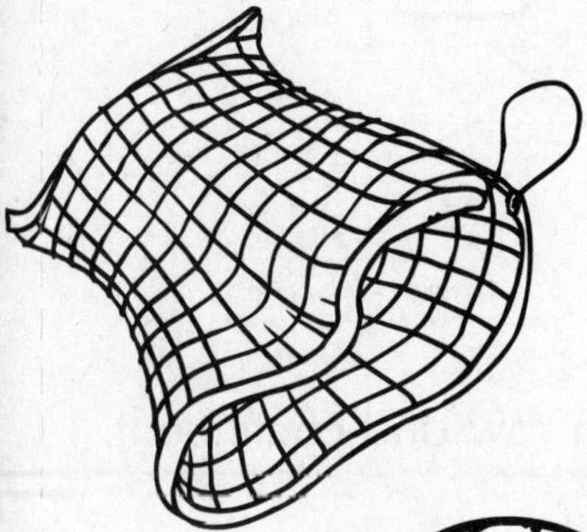

TIP

Underline the ones place. If the number ends in a 0, 2, 4, 6, 8, the number will always be even. If it ends in a 1, 3, 5, 7, 9, the number will always be odd.

The balls fell out of the coach's net! Help the coach collect the balls by writing the numbers in order from **greatest** to **least**. Then color the balls that have even numbers.

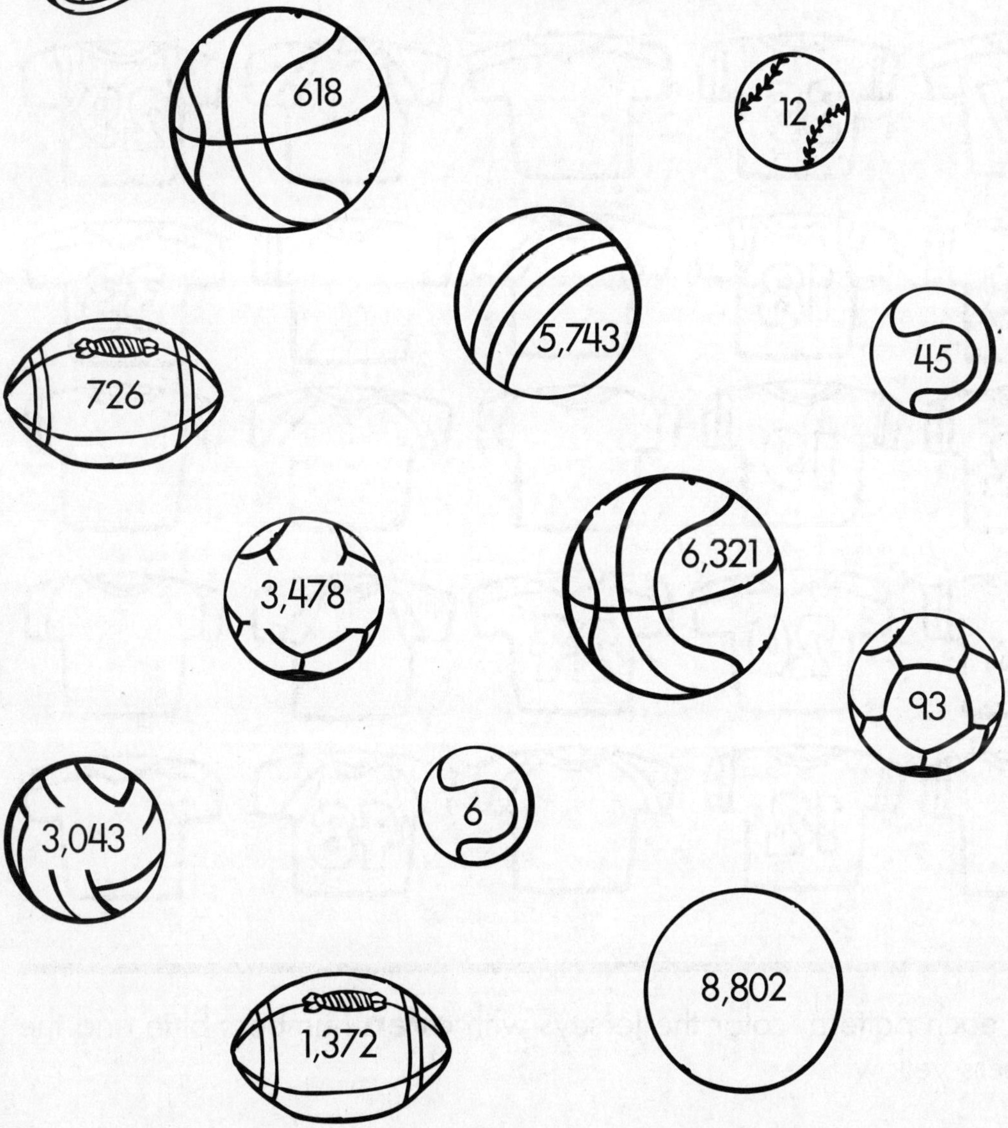

Greatest

____

____

____

____

____

____

____

____

____

____

____

____

Least

Winning Patterns

The pattern is counting by 4's!

Look at the numerals on the jerseys below. Find the pattern for each row and continue it.

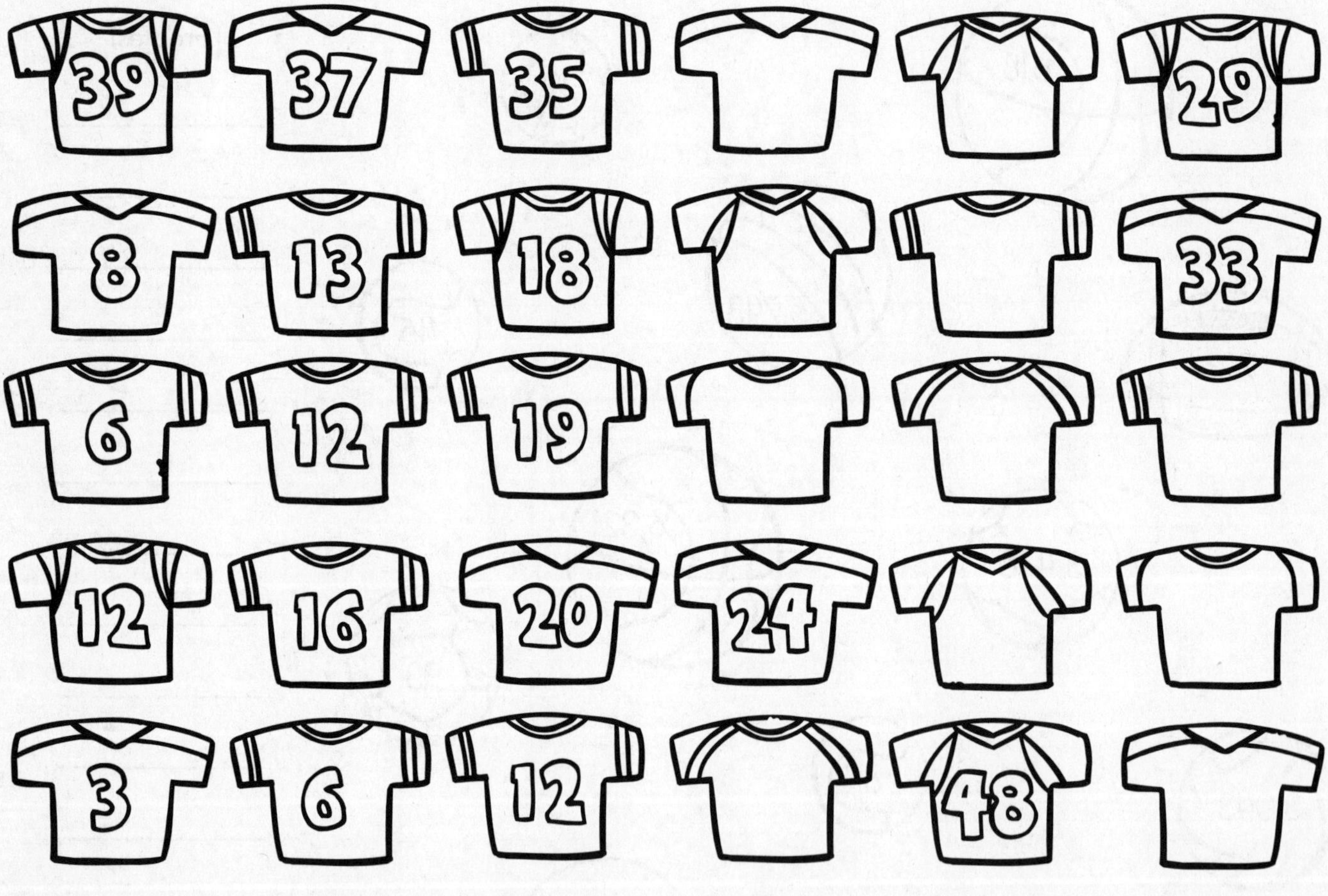

After you've completed each pattern, color the jerseys with **even** numbers blue and the jerseys with **odd** numbers yellow.

How many **even-numbered** jerseys are there? ______________________________

How many **odd-numbered** jerseys are there? ______________________________

Icing the Equations

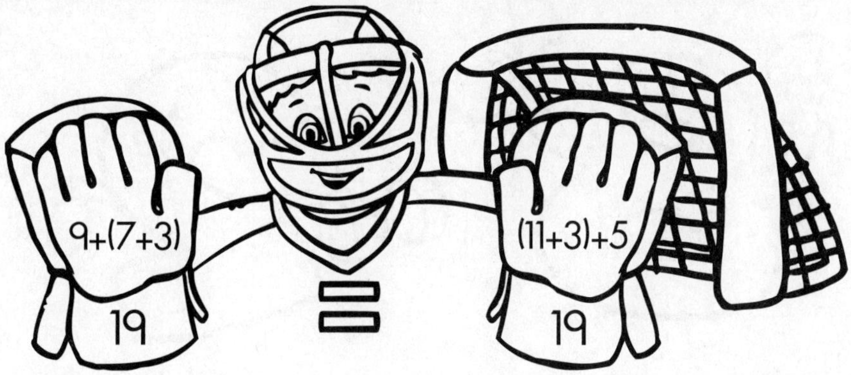

Write the correct symbol (<, >, =, +, −, x, ÷) to make each sentence true.

48 ☐ 62	208 ☐ 179	9 ☐ 5 = 14	7 x 6 ☐ 9 x 9
79 ☐ 7 = 72	4 ☐ 9 = 36	60 ☐ 5 = 12	8 x 6 ☐ 7 x 4
417 ☐ 389 + 28	108 + 9 ☐ 120	40 ☐ 12 x 3	9 x 7 ☐ 12 x 5
573 ☐ 357	306 ☐ 53 = 253	9 x 8 ☐ 12 x 5	32 ÷ 4 ☐ 40 ÷ 5

Write <, >, or = to complete each number sentence.
Remember to do what is in parentheses first!

(12 – 5) +2 ☐ (7 – 5) + 8	(13 + 4) – 7 ☐ (7 x 2) + 9
7 + (6 x 3) ☐ (4 x 3) + 5	8 + (24 ÷ 6) ☐ 9 x (7 + 4)
(12 ÷ 6) + 9 ☐ 8 + (24 ÷ 3)	(56 ÷ 8) + 12 ☐ 48 + (4 x 3)
2 + (16 + 3) ☐ (18 + 3) – 8	5 + (6 x12) ☐ 81 ÷ (16 – 7)
(6 x 3) + 5 ☐ (14 ÷ 7) + 5	14 + (7 x 3) ☐ 36 – (5 x 3)
4 + (7 – 2) ☐ 6 + (10 + 5)	36 – (4 x 7) ☐ (9 x 6) - 25
(6 x 8) + 2 ☐ (35 – 5) + 10 + 10	8 x (4 x 2) ☐ (7 x 7) + 15
5 + 6 + (4 x 5) ☐ (10 – 5) x 5	4 x (6 +3) ☐ 5 + (8 x 2)

Work It Out!

Complete each number sentence using addition, subtraction, multiplication, or division.

Examples: 6 __+__ 2 = 8   6 __–__ 2 = 4   6 __x__ 2 = 12   6 __÷__ 2 = 3

6 ___ 7 = 42   48 ___ 6 = 8   19 ___ 15 = 4

10 ___ 7 = 3   42 ___ 7 = 6   36 ___ 6 = 6

15 ___ 5 = 10   60 ___ 5 = 12   23 ___ 5 = 28

9 ___ 8 = 72   9 ___ 7 = 63

27 ___ 9 = 3

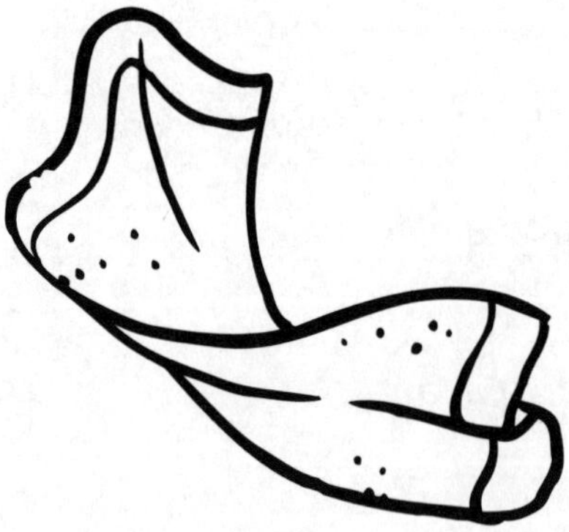

12 ___ 3 = 15   11 ___ 4 = 44

18 ___ 6 = 12   23 ___ 7 = 16

20 ___ 5 = 4   81 ___ 9 = 9

16 ___ 4 = 4   63 ___ 7 = 9

4 ___ 5 = 19   8 ___ 12 = 96   21 ___ 3 = 7

8 ___ 8 = 64   31 ___ 7 = 24

13 ___ 6 = 7   84 ___ 7 = 12

23 ___ 7 = 30

24 ___ 3 = 8

27 ___ 9 = 18

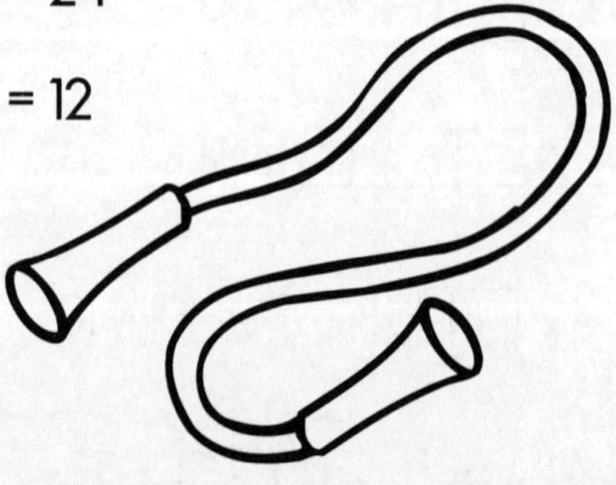

Numbers in Flight

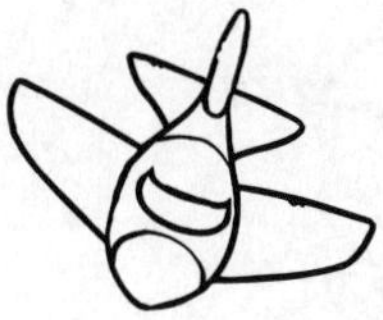

Round the numbers to the nearest tens, hundreds, or thousands.

TIP

Underline the place that it asks you to round. Look to the right of the underlined number. If the number is 5 or more, let it soar. If the number is 4 or less, let it rest.

Tens		**Hundreds**		**Thousands**	
12	______	418	______	6,212	______
26	______	514	______	2,578	______
15	______	1,232	______	5,371	______
367	______	2,785	______	9,786	______
274	______	6,071	______	1,321	______
78	______	942	______	4,736	______
49	______	237	______	7,439	______
63	______	673	______	8,742	______
72	______	52	______	9,417	______
118	______	3,088	______	10,714	______

Keeping Score

Roman Numeral Code:

I=1	IV=4	V=5
IX=9	X=10	XV=15
XX=20	XXX=30	XL=40
L=50		

The scores below are written in standard form.
Use the code to write them in Roman numeral form.

HOME	VISITORS
7	**9**
____	____

HOME	VISITORS
14	**18**
____	____

HOME	VISITORS
17	**6**
____	____

HOME	VISITORS
23	**31**
____	____

HOME	VISITORS
8	**16**
____	____

HOME	VISITORS
19	**33**
____	____

HOME	VISITORS
36	**22**
____	____

HOME	VISITORS
24	**37**
____	____

HOME	VISITORS
50	**38**
____	____

HOME	VISITORS
34	**48**
____	____

HOME	VISITORS
43	**50**
____	____

HOME	VISITORS
54	**27**
____	____

Story Problem Stumpers!

Solve the problems.

1. Susan is making a list of numbers whose digits have a sum of 20. Cross out the number that should not be included on her list.

   5,537 66,404 9,041 992 7,274

2. Mrs. Clayton was buying treats for her children. She bought $12 worth of cinnamon rolls, $9 worth of candy, $8 worth of cookies, and $10 worth of pretzels. Estimate the total amount of money Mrs. Clayton spent.

3. On Friday, 692 people attended a football game at Wyatt Stadium. On Saturday, 934 people attended a soccer game at the same stadium. Estimate how many more people were at the stadium on Saturday than on Friday.

   Approximately how many people were at the stadium on both days combined?

4. The Carter High School Band has been selling raffle tickets for the past four months in order to buy new uniforms. The band sold 2,571 tickets in September, 982 in October, 1,290 in November, and 5,302 in December. Write the amount of tickets sold for the four months in order from greatest to least.

   About how many raffle tickets did the band sell in all?

5. Lacey received a guitar for Christmas. Her goal is to learn to play well by the summer. She practiced her guitar for 7 hours in January, 10 hours in February, and 13 hours in March. If this pattern continues, how many hours will Lacey practice in April?

   How many will she practice in May?

   What is the pattern?

Tasty Treats

Add. Then use the code to color the treats.

Color Code:

Purple	Green	Yellow
under 50	51 to 70	over 70

A Blockbuster Success!

Add. Circle the sums that are **odd** numbers.

437 + 324	526 + 437	612 + 378			
619 + 846	708 +491	792 + 279	437 + 809		
884 + 376	987 + 549	807 + 605	989 + 432	643 + 275	650 + 593
322 + 789	403 + 197	737 + 281	812 + 189	283 + 347	527 +413
803 + 379	902 + 188	543 + 179	817 + 723	425 +578	275 + 337

Sum Popcorn

Add. Mark an **X** on the sum if the number is **even**.

1,598 + 5,269	1,234 + 8,529	6,549 + 3,251	1,224 + 9,872	2,232 + 1,094
1,564 + 6,932	7,727 + 1,236	8,521 + 4,562	2,487 + 4,983	3,987 + 1,870
1,079 + 3,281	2,708 + 1,793	4,805 + 1,389	3,746 + 1,507	5,079 + 1,217
2,748 + 3,005	6,417 + 3,723	9,009 + 2,703	5,408 + 1,783	8,175 + 7,027
6,318 + 1,584	5,726 + 2,375	2,275 + 1,750	3,127 + 1,734	4,025 + 5,140

Falling Amounts

Subtract.

938 – 337	657 – 426	549 – 146	486 – 346	748 – 315
432 – 212	860 – 630	354 – 121	762 – 341	388 – 157
576 – 145	927 – 203	659 – 438	284 – 272	743 – 430
767 – 564	849 – 317	983 – 831	454 – 213	788 – 273
939 – 427	748 – 536	965 – 145	847 – 346	876 – 533

Gardening Troubles

Why was the farmer looking for his keys in the garden?

Solve the problems. Then write the letters below to answer the riddle.

52 − 23 = 29 T	36 − 27 Y	65 − 48 H	93 − 8 S	71 − 65 I
97 − 59 T	75 − 29 D	85 − 18 H	57 − 49 N	61 − 13 E
68 − 39 O	46 − 18 U	33 − 19 R	56 − 8 E	71 − 15 I
32 − 16 W	41 − 36 H	63 − 38 A	40 − 28 P	51 − 38 N
74 − 25 W	55 − 36 G			

__ __   __ __ __   __ __ __ __ __ __   __ __ __ __ __

67 48   49 25 85   5 29 12 6 8 19   29 17 48 9 46

__ __ __ __ __ __.

38 28 14 13 56 12

A Garden of Good Subtraction

Solve the problems. Check your subtraction with addition!

1. 3,712 − 1,895 = 1,817 1,817 + 1,895 = 3,712	2. 7,406 − 3,677
3. 3,413 − 1,798	4. 5,935 − 2,329
5. 3,009 − 1,998	6. 6,187 − 2,789
7. 4,108 − 2,299	8. 2,112 − 998

Round the answers to the subtraction problems to the nearest thousand.

1. ______ 2. ______ 3. ______ 4. ______

5. ______ 6. ______ 7. ______ 8. ______

Shopping Success

Add. Don't forget to line up your decimals!

$148.78 + 16.99	$16.75 + 23.89	$215.89 + 347.23	$107.50 + 341.98
$435.28 + 143.22	$309.78 + 477.45	$706.29 + 88.39	$700.99 + 199.64
$1,079.52 + 8,403.78	$2,783.25 + 103.65	$7,089.18 + 84.23	$2,307.13 + 879.56
$9,078.44 + 3,445.97	$5,655.39 + 1,454.63	$3,905.17 + 7,108.82	$8,805.94 + 6,397.18

After you've solved the problems, do the following. (Round to the nearest thousand.)

1. Circle the sums that can be rounded between $1,000 and $5,000.
2. Mark an X on the sums that can be rounded between $6,000 and $10,000.
3. Draw a box around the sums that can be rounded between $11,000 and $15,000.

Fruitful Fun with Decimals

4.927		3.690
– 1.237	↗	+1.237
3.690		4.927

Remember to line up your decimals!

Subtract. Then use addition to check your answers.

1.23 – 0.16	+	6.58 – 3.24	+	92.36 – 21.55	+
2.36 – 1.20	+	5.03 – 0.78	+	16.25 – 10.16	+
85.21 – 16.76	+	52.89 – 25.13	+	17.23 – 16.78	+
18.56 – 4.74	+	23.79 – 16.83	+	43.28 – 15.79	+

Story Problems . . . Downloading

Solve the problems.

1. Blaine saw a computer for $475.00 and a printer for $135.00. He decided this was a good deal and just what he needed. In order to buy the computer, Blaine worked each week for three months. He earned $136.00 in March, $231.00 in April, and $179.00 in May. Has Blaine earned enough money to buy the computer and printer? If so, how much will he have left after making the purchase?

2. Lilly was playing a computer game about traveling across the United States. The object of this game is to keep track of the miles traveled. In the first round of the game, Lilly traveled 413 miles. In the second round, she encountered many problems and traveled only 281 miles. She had a successful third round and traveled 674 miles. What is the approximate total number of miles that Lilly traveled in the game?

3. Several of the students in Mrs. Dee's computer class were trying to decide who was the oldest. Carter is younger than Leigh, but older than Kendra. Mark is between Kendra and Carter. List the students from oldest to youngest.

4. The technology students have been studying the rise in population in their city over the past ten years in order to produce graphs. In the first three years, the population increased by 3,716 people. In the next four years, the population went up again by 4,119 people. Finally, in the past three years, it increased by 9,658 people. What is the total number of people the population has increased by over the past ten years?

5. The Cunningham High School Technology Team logs the amount of minutes they spend on the computer each month. In September, they logged 3,107 minutes. In October, they were busy with projects and logged a total of 8,983 minutes for the month. How many more minutes did the technology team log in October than in September?

Multiplication Madness

Complete the multiplication table. Do you see the pattern?

x	1	2	3	4	5	6	7	8	9	10
1	1									
2										
3										
4										
5										
6										
7										
8										
9										
10										

A fact family looks like this: 6 x 7 = 42, 7 x 6 = 42, 42 ÷ 6 = 7, 42 ÷ 7 = 6
Create a fact family using the numbers 2, 5, and 10.

Speeding Along

Solve the problems as fast as you can. Time yourself or ask someone to time you.

8 x 3	7 x 9	5 x 3	8 x 7	9 x 3	6 x 5	1 x 9
3 x 4	6 x 6	8 x 9	6 x 4	4 x 9	5 x 7	4 x 5
9 x 5	8 x 8	6 x 7	7 x 9	3 x 8	2 x 2	3 x 2
1 x 3	0 x 9	8 x 6	7 x 3	4 x 4	3 x 3	7 x 3
9 x 9	5 x 4	3 x 9	2 x 7	1 x 8	8 x 5	8 x 2
7 x 7	6 x 3	3 x 2	4 x 0	8 x 4	0 x 8	6 x 0
9 x 7	5 x 2	3 x 6	8 x 9	6 x 7	7 x 2	9 x 3

Time: __________ Missed ______ out of 49

A Fresh Batch of Multiplication

Step 1:	1 24 x **4** 6	Multiply the ones place first **(4 x 4 = 16)**. Write the **6** in the ones place. Write the **1** ten above so you remember it.
Step 2:	1 24 x **4** **96**	Now, multiply the tens place (**2** tens x **4** = **8** tens). Then add the **1** ten (**1**+**8**=**9**)

Multiply.

12 x 8	23 x 9	19 x 6	14 x 3	34 x 6	15 x 4
33 x 5	43 x 4	29 x 2	45 x 4	17 x 5	35 x 8
18 x 3	13 x 6	32 x 7	28 x 3	42 x 9	26 x 5
25 x 3	34 x 4	27 x 2	16 x 4	22 x 7	44 x 3

Moving Along with Multiplication

High-Flying Multiplication

A. 1 23 x14 (multiply the ones first) 2	B. 1 23 x14 92 (don't forget to add the ten you carried)
C. 1 23 x14 92 230 (use a 0 to hold the one's place)	D. 23 x14 92 230 (add) **322**

Multiply.

28 x 33	43 x 48	52 x 29	63 x 19	56 x 15
38 x 24	68 x 18	73 x 14	91 x 54	17 x 23
72 x 39	84 x 17	29 x 28	56 x 23	36 x 18
72 x 25	17 x 90	51 x 47	45 x 82	54 x 13

Fast Forward with Multiplication

A.	B.	C.
H T O	H T O	H T O
	2 1	2 1
343	**343**	343
x 5**2**	x **5**2	x 52
686	686	686
	1,715**0**	+17150
		17,836
Multiply the ones.	**Multiply the tens.**	**Then add it all up!**

Multiply.

391 x 24	478 x 62	927 x 45	841 x 29	614 x 83
597 x 51	658 x 73	743 x 16	126 x 38	239 x 15
415 x 14	807 x 86	193 x 19	485 x 23	318 x 17
312 x 33	451 x 12	312 x 50	902 x 74	605 x 28

And They're Off

Solve the problems as fast as you can. Time yourself or ask someone to time you.

$7\overline{)56}$	$9\overline{)36}$	$6\overline{)42}$	$9\overline{)27}$	$7\overline{)63}$	$4\overline{)24}$	$8\overline{)56}$
$5\overline{)25}$	$8\overline{)0}$	$4\overline{)8}$	$5\overline{)45}$	$4\overline{)28}$	$7\overline{)35}$	$7\overline{)49}$
$9\overline{)18}$	$8\overline{)8}$	$6\overline{)18}$	$7\overline{)14}$	$2\overline{)8}$	$6\overline{)54}$	$9\overline{)18}$
$7\overline{)0}$	$6\overline{)12}$	$3\overline{)6}$	$8\overline{)72}$	$9\overline{)63}$	$3\overline{)24}$	$8\overline{)64}$
$8\overline{)24}$	$5\overline{)40}$	$4\overline{)32}$	$3\overline{)15}$	$6\overline{)30}$	$5\overline{)5}$	$5\overline{)25}$
$4\overline{)4}$	$9\overline{)45}$	$7\overline{)21}$	$8\overline{)40}$	$3\overline{)9}$	$2\overline{)14}$	$9\overline{)72}$
$8\overline{)56}$	$4\overline{)12}$	$2\overline{)0}$	$6\overline{)30}$	$2\overline{)8}$	$8\overline{)48}$	$6\overline{)36}$

Time: ____________ Missed ______ out of 49

Leaping Lizards Long Division

$$\begin{array}{r} 9\text{ r}2 \\ 8\overline{)74} \\ \underline{-72} \\ 2 \end{array}$$

Divide to find the quotient. Watch out for remainders!

$7\overline{)49}$ $5\overline{)20}$ $7\overline{)66}$ $8\overline{)47}$ $9\overline{)62}$ $4\overline{)30}$

$2\overline{)14}$ $8\overline{)69}$ $3\overline{)23}$ $7\overline{)42}$ $9\overline{)18}$ $5\overline{)37}$

$9\overline{)88}$ $6\overline{)55}$ $7\overline{)35}$ $7\overline{)53}$ $2\overline{)10}$ $8\overline{)64}$

$2\overline{)16}$ $7\overline{)69}$ $3\overline{)15}$ $4\overline{)35}$ $9\overline{)45}$ $9\overline{)81}$

Dog Gone Division

Divide.

5)655	2)144	4)364	6)240	7)455
8)224	5)235	2)122	7)560	6)552
9)279	3)156	3)189	4)428	3)753
5)425	6)456	7)126	8)656	5)630

Take the Challenge!

Divide.

217 7)1,519 −14 11 −7 49 −49 0	8)4,378	4)2,578	9)8,327	8)7,613
6)3,487	5)1,575	3)4,179	6)1,938	2)1,675
7)2,577	8)2,496	5)2,673	4)1,725	3)2,674

Think About It

Solve the problems. Show your work!

1. Kelli bought a new photo album to display her vacation pictures. Each page of the album displays six photos. There are a total of 143 pages in the book. How many photos can the album hold?

   If Kelli has 964 photos, how many more pages does she need?

2. Farmer Joe has many chickens on his farm. Every week he collects and fills 238 cartons of eggs to take to the market. Each carton can hold 12 eggs. What is the total number of eggs that Farmer Joe collects in one week?

3. Sophie enjoys reading. Over the past week and a half, Sophie has read seven books with a total of 966 pages. If all seven books have the same number of pages, which number sentence can be used to find the number of pages in each book?

   a. 966 + 7 = ___ b. 966 x 7 = ___ c. 966 ÷ 7 = ___ d. 966 – 7 = ___

   How many pages were in each book?

4. Kendra's father is a carpenter. Last week he repaired Mrs. Gibson's deck. He worked for six hours a day for two days until the job was complete. Kendra's father then billed Mrs. Gibson for $45.00 an hour. What was the total amount that Mrs. Gibson had to pay?

5. Jesse had 93 miniature racecars and 87 semi-trucks. The toy tracks that he has will make up ten different roads. Jesse wants to put an equal number of vehicles on each road. How many vehicles can he put on each road?

Delicious Fractions

Color the correct amount.

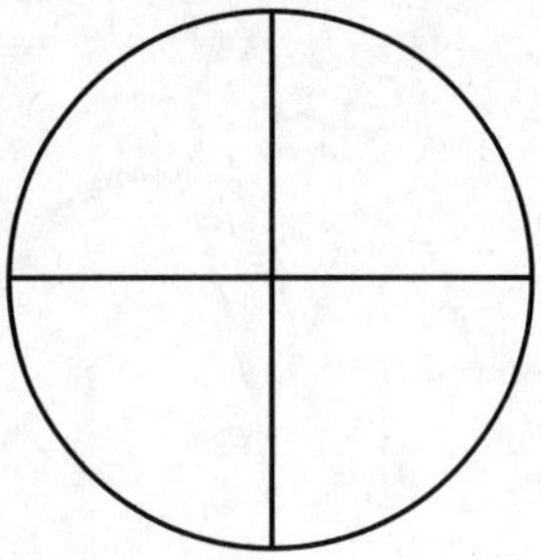

$= \frac{3}{4}$

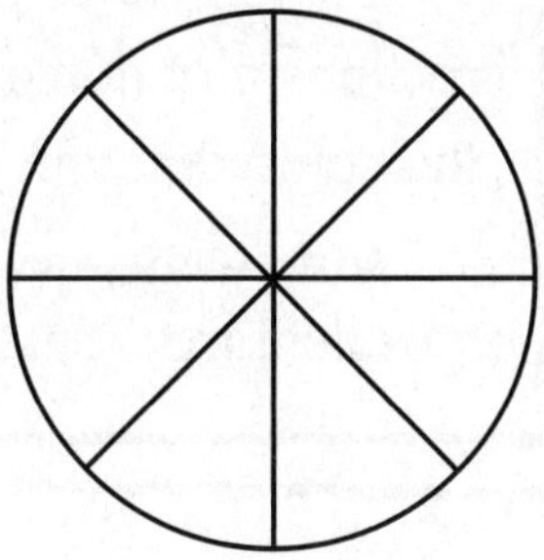

$= \frac{3}{8}$

$= \frac{4}{8}$

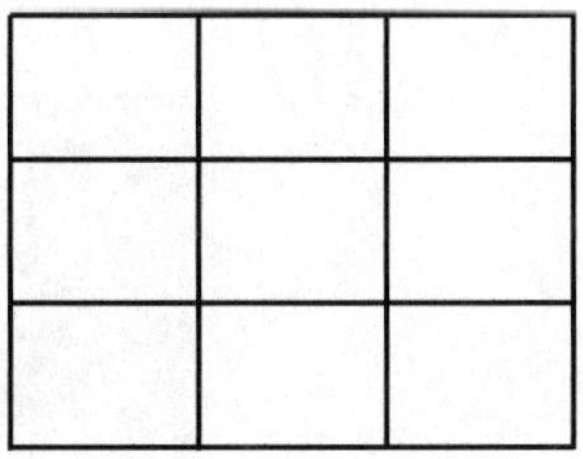

$= \frac{3}{9}$

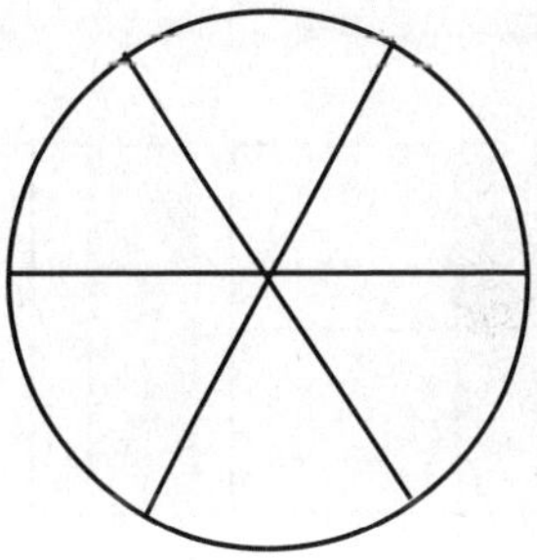

$= \frac{4}{6}$

Draw a picture and color part of it to show the fraction.

$\frac{7}{8} =$	$\frac{4}{10} =$	$\frac{3}{5} =$
$\frac{2}{5} =$	$\frac{2}{7} =$	$\frac{5}{6} =$

Fraction Double Take

Write the **equivalent** fraction.

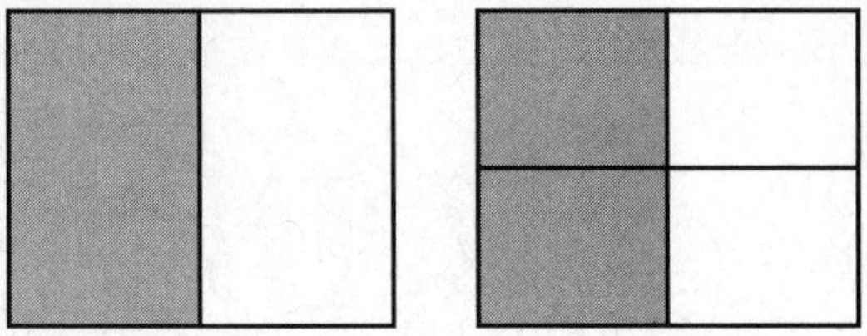

$\frac{1}{2} = \frac{2}{4}$

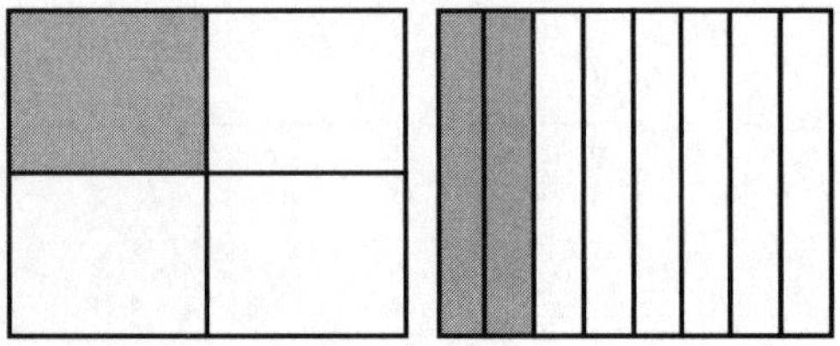

$\frac{1}{4} = \frac{\quad}{8}$

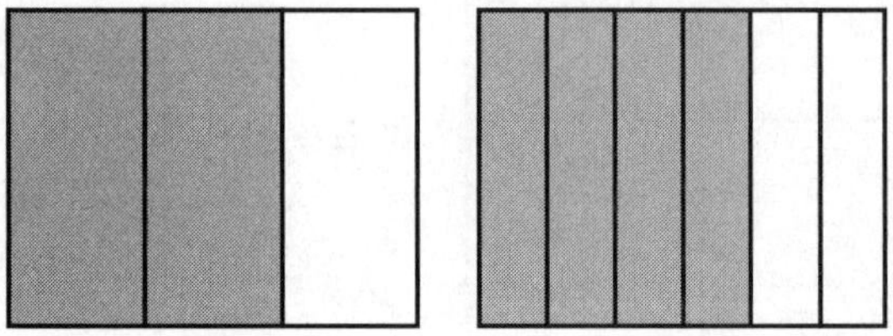

$\frac{2}{3} = \frac{\quad}{6}$

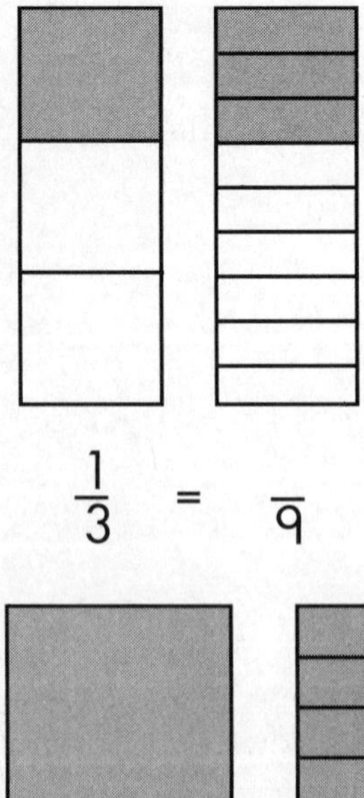

$\frac{1}{3} = \frac{\quad}{9}$

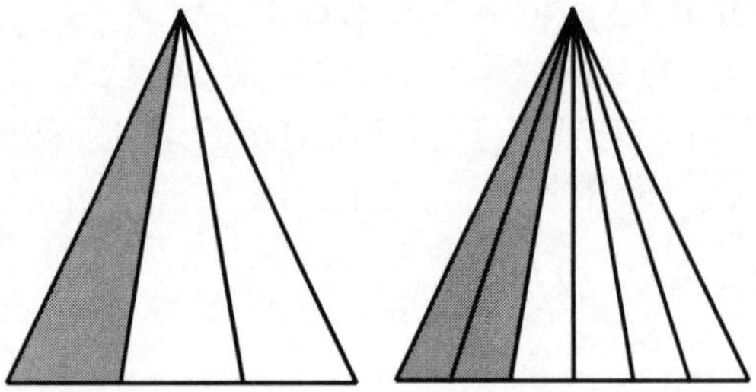

$\frac{1}{3} = \frac{\quad}{6}$

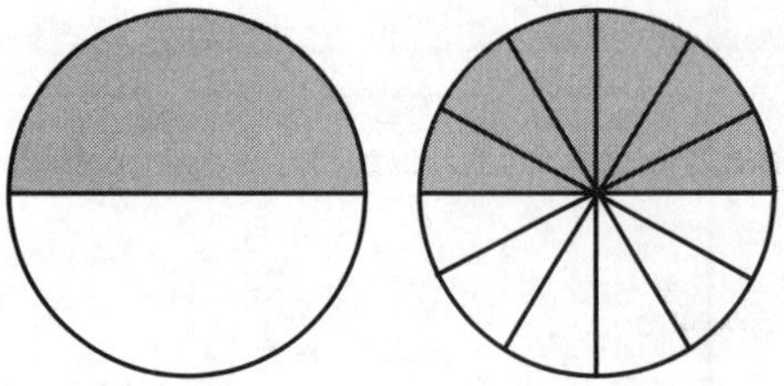

$\frac{1}{2} = \frac{\quad}{12}$

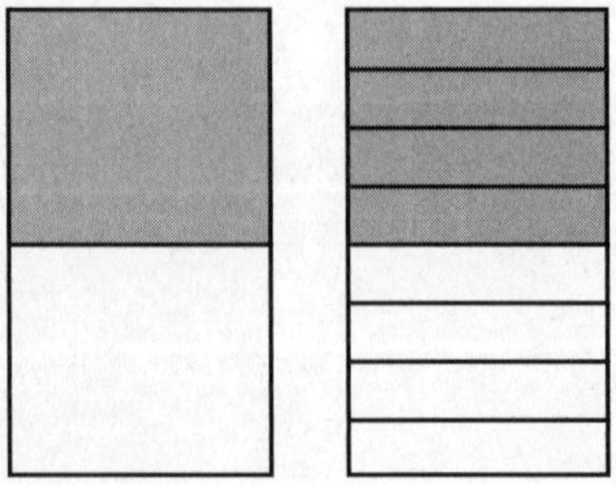

$\frac{1}{2} = \frac{\quad}{8}$

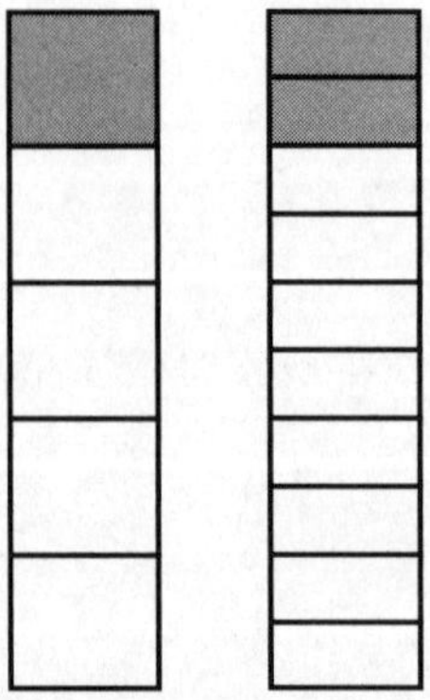

$\frac{1}{5} = \frac{\quad}{10}$

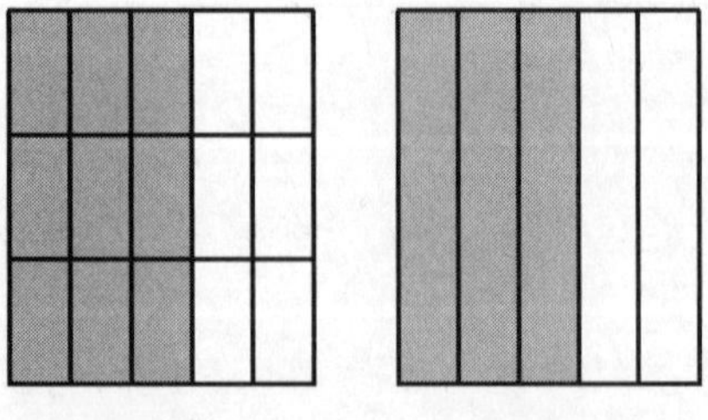

$\frac{9}{15} = \frac{\quad}{5}$

Fraction Review I

Shade the correct number triangles to show the fraction.
Then write the number that you shaded.

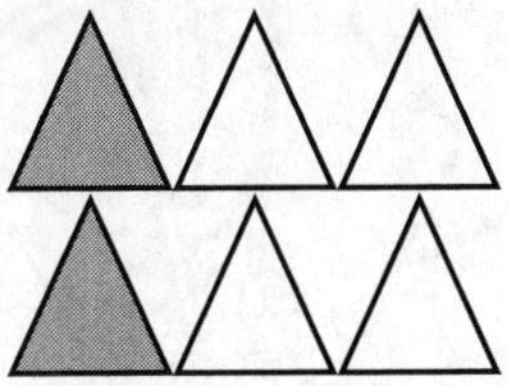

$\frac{1}{3}$ of 6 = 2

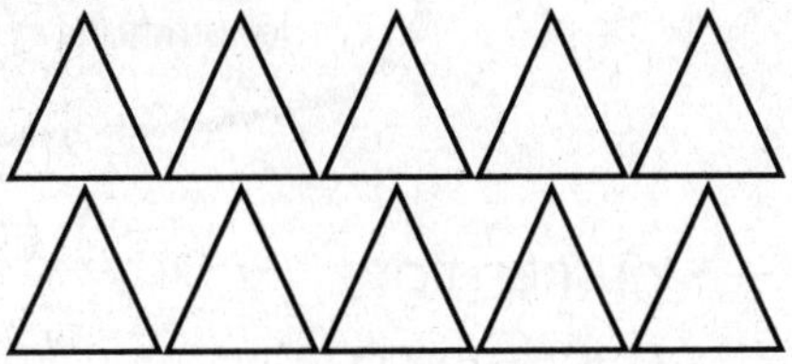

$\frac{1}{5}$ of 10 = ___

$\frac{1}{3}$ of 9 = ___

$\frac{1}{2}$ of 4 = ___

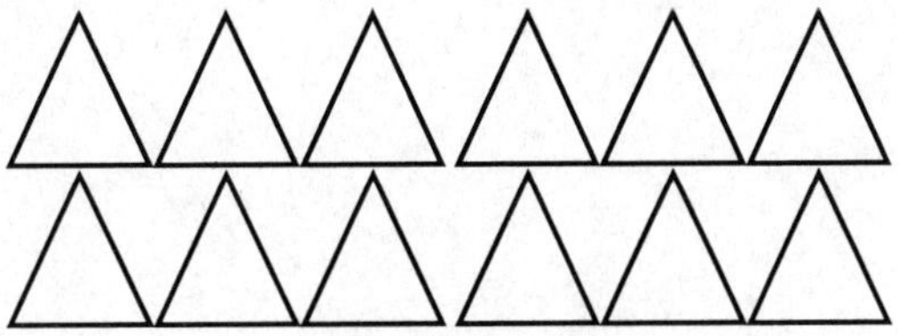

$\frac{1}{4}$ of 12 = ___

$\frac{2}{3}$ of 9 = ___

Draw the correct number of circles and shade the number of parts shown.
Then write the fraction for the shaded area.

6 circles 3 parts =_____	8 circles 2 parts =_____	10 circles 5 parts =_____
12 circles 4 parts =_____	15 circles 3 parts =_____	6 circles 2 parts =_____

Adding it Up

$\frac{1}{6} + \frac{3}{6} = \frac{4}{6}$ → numerator / → denominator

Add.

$\frac{2}{6} + \frac{4}{6} =$ $\frac{1}{5} + \frac{1}{5} =$ $\frac{4}{16} + \frac{7}{16} =$

$\frac{6}{10} + \frac{3}{10} =$ $\frac{1}{9} + \frac{6}{9} =$ $\frac{5}{8} + \frac{2}{8} =$

$\frac{5}{9} + \frac{1}{9} =$ $\frac{2}{7} + \frac{1}{7} =$ $\frac{2}{6} + \frac{3}{6} =$

$\frac{2}{10} + \frac{7}{10} =$ $\frac{1}{12} + \frac{3}{12} =$ $\frac{3}{9} + \frac{4}{9} =$

$\frac{3}{8} + \frac{5}{8} =$ $\frac{3}{5} + \frac{1}{5} =$ $\frac{5}{12} + \frac{6}{12} =$

$\frac{7}{16} + \frac{4}{16} =$ $\frac{5}{10} + \frac{3}{10} =$ $\frac{6}{14} + \frac{1}{14} =$

$\frac{4}{8} + \frac{2}{8} =$ $\frac{3}{15} + \frac{7}{15} =$ $\frac{3}{12} + \frac{7}{12} =$

Fraction Review II

Solve the fraction problems. Remember to watch your signs.

$\frac{1}{6} + \frac{2}{6} = \frac{3}{6}$	$\frac{3}{5} - \frac{1}{5} =$	$\frac{5}{12} + \frac{6}{12} =$
$\frac{5}{9} + \frac{1}{9} =$	$\frac{7}{10} + \frac{2}{10} =$	$\frac{6}{12} - \frac{2}{12} =$
$\frac{7}{9} - \frac{5}{9} =$	$\frac{9}{10} - \frac{5}{10} =$	$\frac{2}{3} - \frac{1}{3} =$
$\frac{7}{8} - \frac{3}{8} =$	$\frac{3}{7} + \frac{1}{7} =$	$\frac{5}{8} + \frac{2}{8} =$
$\frac{4}{16} + \frac{4}{16} =$	$\frac{8}{12} + \frac{2}{12} =$	$\frac{9}{12} - \frac{4}{12} =$
$\frac{7}{10} - \frac{4}{10} =$	$\frac{6}{9} + \frac{2}{9} =$	$\frac{8}{16} - \frac{4}{16} =$
$\frac{5}{15} + \frac{10}{15} =$	$\frac{7}{16} - \frac{5}{16} =$	$\frac{9}{12} + \frac{2}{12} =$

Fun with Fractions

Finding the greatest common factors for both numbers can be easy!

Simplify those fractions!

$\frac{8}{32}$ List all the factors that equal the numerator! (1,2,4,⑧)
List all the factors that equal the denominator! (1,2,4,⑧,32)

Now, circle the greatest common factor!

Write down the **common factors** for the numerators and denominators below.
Circle the **greatest common factor** for each fraction.

$\frac{6}{18}$ ______ ______

$\frac{6}{24}$ ______ ______

$\frac{9}{36}$ ______ ______

$\frac{7}{42}$ ______ ______

$\frac{9}{81}$ ______ ______

$\frac{8}{48}$ ______ ______

$\frac{12}{36}$ ______ ______

$\frac{14}{28}$ ______ ______

Example: $\frac{3 \div 3}{6 \div 3} = \frac{1}{2}$

1st – Find the greatest common factor of the numerator and denominator.
2nd – Divide both the numerator and denominator by that number.

Congratulations! You've just simplified that fraction!

Simplify the fractions.

$\frac{4}{12}$ = ___ $\frac{5}{25}$ = ___ $\frac{7}{28}$ = ___ $\frac{6}{48}$ = ___ $\frac{8}{72}$ = ___

$\frac{12}{24}$ = ___ $\frac{14}{21}$ = ___ $\frac{4}{32}$ = ___ $\frac{7}{63}$ = ___ $\frac{9}{36}$ = ___

$\frac{3}{18}$ = ___ $\frac{9}{27}$ = ___ $\frac{6}{12}$ = ___ $\frac{12}{48}$ = ___ $\frac{9}{12}$ = ___

$\frac{5}{20}$ = ___ $\frac{8}{16}$ = ___ $\frac{7}{21}$ = ___ $\frac{16}{48}$ = ___ $\frac{12}{18}$ = ___

Different, but the SAME!

Write the **fraction** and **mixed numeral** for

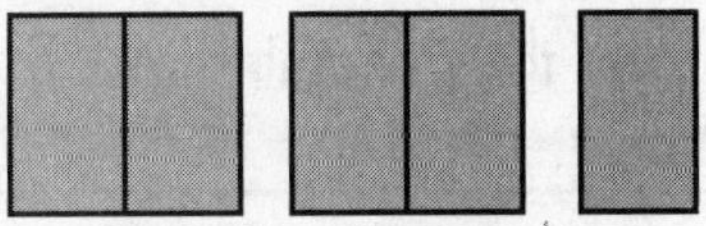

$\frac{5}{2}$ $2\frac{1}{2}$

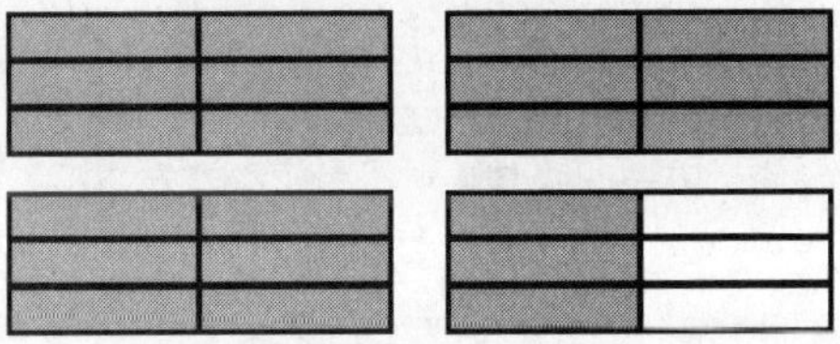

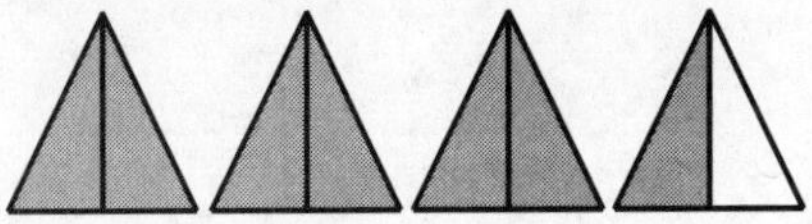

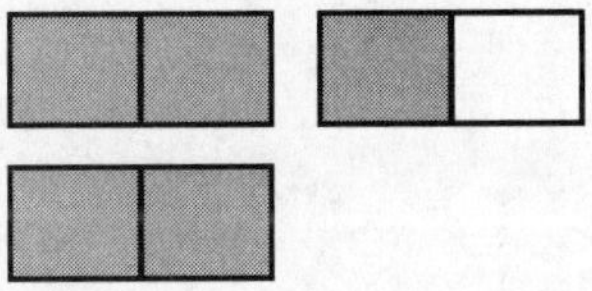

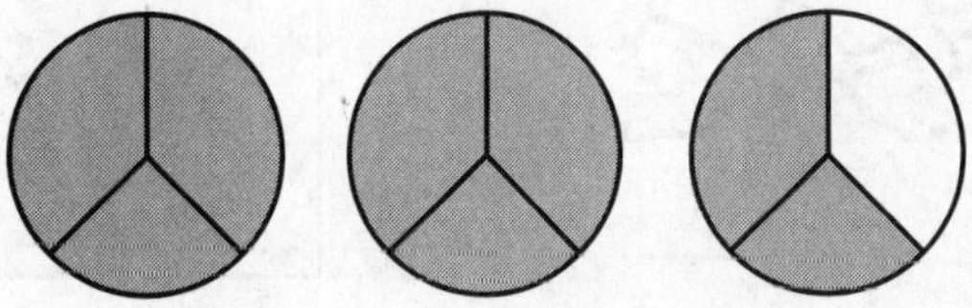

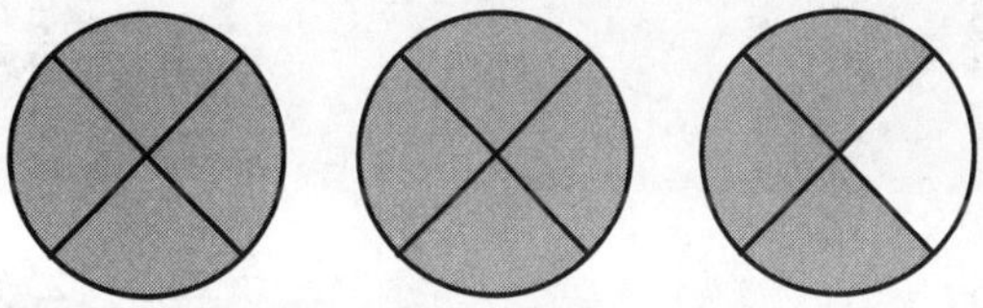

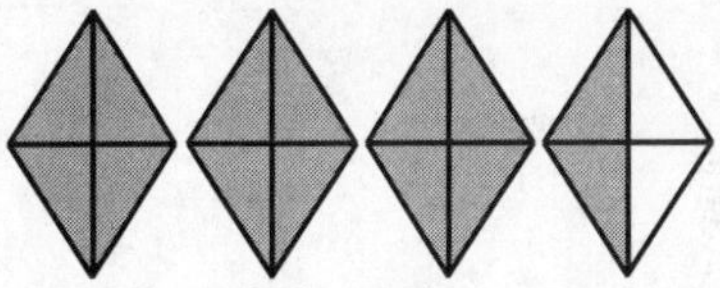

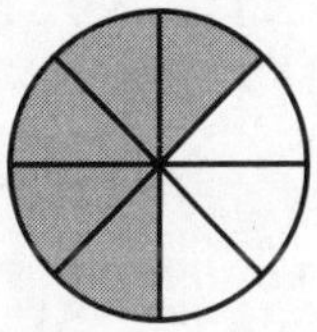

That's Top Heavy

An improper fraction is a top heavy fraction.

The numerator the denominator $\frac{32}{9}$ is larger than so it's top heavy!

Here's how to convert a mixed number to an improper fraction.

$3\frac{5}{9}$

Step 1: Take the whole number (3).
Step 2: Multiply it by the denominator (9). $3 \times 9 = 27$
Step 3: Add the numerator (5). $27 + 5 = 32$
Step 4: Place the total over the denominator (9). $\frac{32}{9}$

Write the mixed number as an **improper fraction.**

$2\frac{3}{4} = \frac{11}{4}$	$6\frac{4}{5} =$	$8\frac{4}{7} =$
$4\frac{5}{8} =$	$7\frac{3}{7} =$	$5\frac{2}{9} =$
$8\frac{3}{4} =$	$5\frac{1}{2} =$	$3\frac{4}{8} =$
$3\frac{2}{9} =$	$7\frac{5}{9} =$	$7\frac{2}{4} =$
$2\frac{1}{4} =$	$2\frac{3}{7} =$	$3\frac{5}{7} =$
$5\frac{3}{8} =$	$4\frac{1}{6} =$	$1\frac{7}{9} =$
$5\frac{2}{8} =$	$6\frac{3}{5} =$	$8\frac{3}{5} =$
$1\frac{5}{9} =$	$8\frac{4}{9} =$	$2\frac{7}{8} =$

What's the Value?

Hundreds	Tens	Ones	•	Tenths	Hundredths
				2	

$= \frac{2}{10}$

Decimal (the • is the decimal)

A decimal is a number that uses place value and a decimal to show value less than a whole (or one).

A fraction does the same thing. So fractions and decimals mean the same thing. They are just written a little differently.

This whole is divided into tenths.

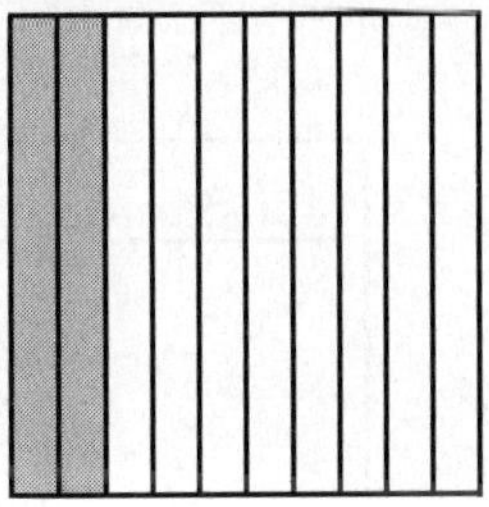

$\frac{2}{10} = .2$

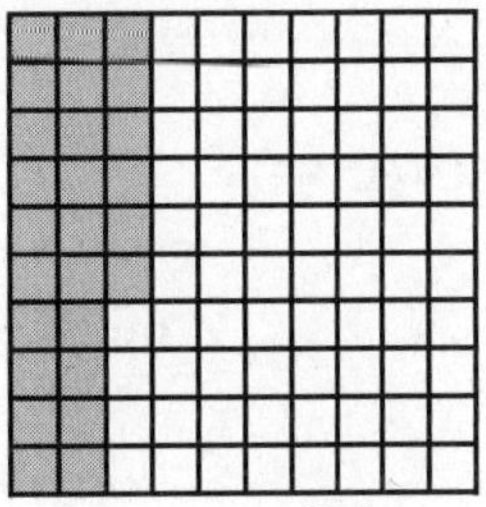

$.26 = \frac{26}{100}$

This whole is divided into hundredths.

Write the **fraction** and the **decimal number** for each.

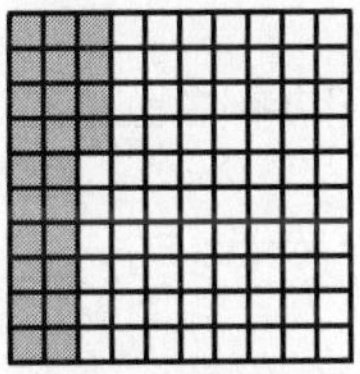

____ = ____

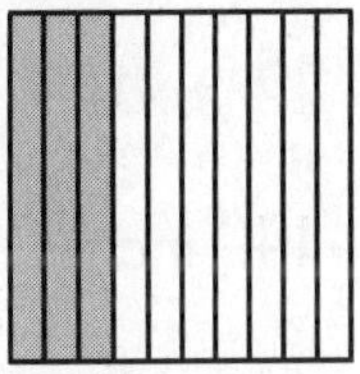

____ = ____

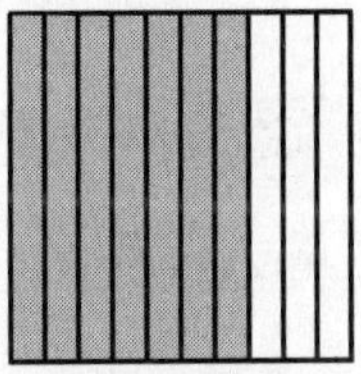

____ = ____

____ = ____

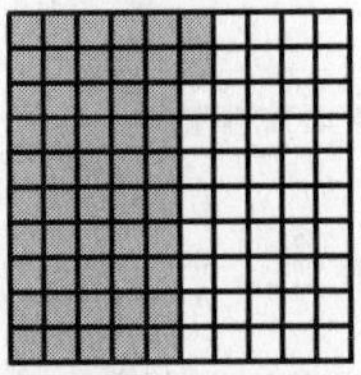

____ = ____

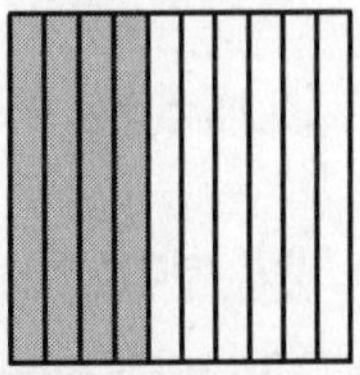

____ = ____

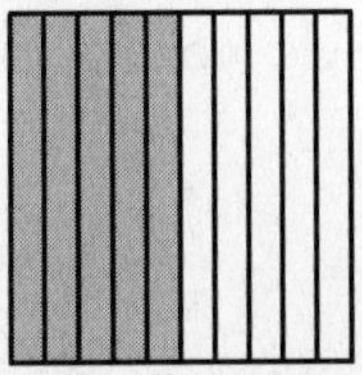

____ = ____

____ = ____

Changing Units

The Golden Rule

When you change larger units to smaller units, you multiply.

Example: 4 yards x 3 feet = 12 feet

When you change smaller units to larger units, you divide.

Example: 36 inches ÷ 12 feet = 3 feet

Convert each unit of measure.

Customary Units for Linear Measures

12 inches = 1 foot
3 feet = 1 yard
5,280 feet = 1 mile
1,760 yards = 1 mile

9 feet = ____ yards	2 miles = ____ feet	
36 inches = ____ yards	9 yards = ____ feet	
48 inches = ____ feet	60 inches = ____ feet	
7 feet = ____ inches	96 inches = ____ feet	9 feet = ____ inches
36 feet = ____ yards	12 yards = ____ inches	3 miles = ____ yards
3,520 yards = ____ miles	144 inches = ____ feet	18 yards = ____ inches
5 yards = ____ feet	5 miles = ____ feet	46 feet = ____ inches
6 feet = ____ yards	12 feet = ____ inches	48 feet = ____ yards
3 miles = ____ feet	9 miles = ____ yards	72 inches = ____ feet
14 feet = ____ inches	2 miles = ____ feet	24 feet = ____ yards
6 yards = ____ inches	30 yards = ____ feet	84 inches = ____ feet
21 feet = ____ yards	10 yards = ____ inches	4 miles = ____ feet

If fencing is $2.00 per foot, how much would it cost to fence a dog run with a 36-yard perimeter for Brutus to have fun in?

The Rule of Thumb

Remember to multiply when you change larger units to smaller units and to divide when you change smaller units to larger units.

<u>Customary Units for Measuring Liquids</u>
1 pint = 2 cups (c.)
1 quart = 2 pints (pt.)
1 gallon = 4 quarts (qt.)

<u>Customary Units For Measuring Weight</u>
16 ounces (oz) = 1 pound (lb.)
2,000 lbs = 1 ton (T.)

Circle the more reasonable measurement.

300 T. or 300 lbs.

4 oz. or 4 lbs.

14 oz. or 14 lbs.

10 lbs. or 10 T.

15 T. or 15 lbs.

1 lb. or 1 oz.

15 lb. or 15 oz.

Convert each unit of measure.

8 cups = ______qt.　　2 lb = ______oz.　　3 pt = ______c.

3 gal = ______qt.　　64 oz = ______lb.　　2 gal = ______pt.

1 qt = ______c.　　4 T = ______lb.　　3 qt = ______c.

12 pt = ______c.　　3 lbs = ______oz.　　8 lb = ______oz.

3 qt = ______c.　　6 pt = ______c.　　5 gal = ______qt.

Tony needs four cups of cream for a pie. The store sells cream in one-pint containers. How many pints should Tony buy?

Where in the World

Customary Units For Measuring Time
60 seconds = 1 minute
60 minutes = 1 hour
24 hours = 1 day

Solve the problems.

1. Clay spends seven hours each day at school. He goes to school Monday through Friday. About how many hours does Clay spend at school in one week?

2. Craig's guitar lessons were two hours long. If his lesson ended at 6:15, what time did it begin?

3. Cheryl spent the day cleaning. It took her 25 minutes to vacuum, 18 minutes to dust, and 90 minutes to do the laundry. How many minutes did she spend cleaning?

   How many hours?

4. Barbara exercised for 24 minutes. Then she watched television for 40 minutes. Did the two activities combined take more or less than an hour?

5. Abbey sleeps for ten hours. Then she takes her friends to the mall for six hours and the water park for seven hours. Finally, Abbey spends two hours eating meals and helping her mom around the house. Will she be able to do everything in one day? Explain your answer.

Challenge yourself!
Create a list of things that you do that take a second, minute, hour, or day.

Elapsed Time

Saturday Movie Times at Cinema Town	
10:00 a.m.	**Smokey Town**
11:45 a.m.	**The Pink Cat**
12:15 p.m.	**Julie's Wish**
3:30 p.m.	**Emma's Challenge**

1. All the movies last 2 hours and 10 minutes. At what time will each movie end?

2. If Elizabeth had to walk home after the 3:30 p.m. showing of Emma's Challenge and it took her 20 minutes to walk home, at what time would she get home?

3. Lloyd arrived at Cinema Town at 9:00 a.m. He was able to stay long enough to watch Smokey Town and Emma's Challenge. How long did Lloyd stay at the movies?

4. How much time is there between the end of The Pink Cat and the beginning of Emma's Challenge?

5. Don and Mark are going to the movies. The movie theater is closer to Mark's house and it takes 15 minutes to get there. If it takes Don 10 minutes to walk to Mark's house and they want to leave in time to see The Pink Cat what time will Don need to leave his house?

Complete the charts.

Start Time	End Time	Elapsed Time
1:15 a.m.	______	50 min.
7:30 a.m.	5:25 p.m.	______

Start Time	End Time	Elapsed Time
1:30 p.m.	2:40 p.m.	______
3:45 p.m.	5:15 p.m.	______

Start Time	End Time	Elapsed Time
7:30 p.m.	______	1 hr., 13 min.
8:15 p.m.	______	40 min.

Start Time	End Time	Elapsed Time
2:15 p.m.	7:30 p.m.	______
5:45 p.m.	______	1 hr., 20 min.

Perimeter, It's What's Around You!

Perimeter is the distance around a figure.
To find the perimeter of a shape or figure, add all the sides.

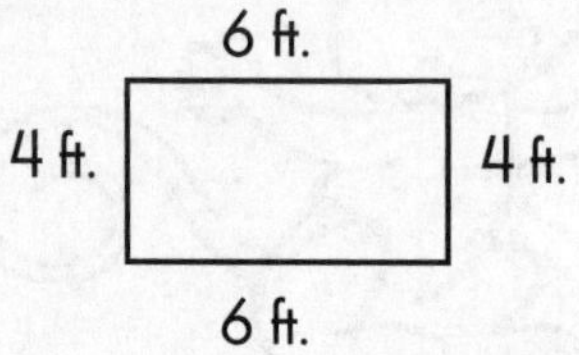

4 ft. + 4 ft. = 8 ft. and 6 ft. + 6 ft. = 12 ft.

OR

4 ft. x 2 sides = 8 ft. and 6 ft. x 2 sides = 12 ft.

8 ft. + 12 ft. = 20 ft. in perimeter

Find the **perimeter** of each shape.

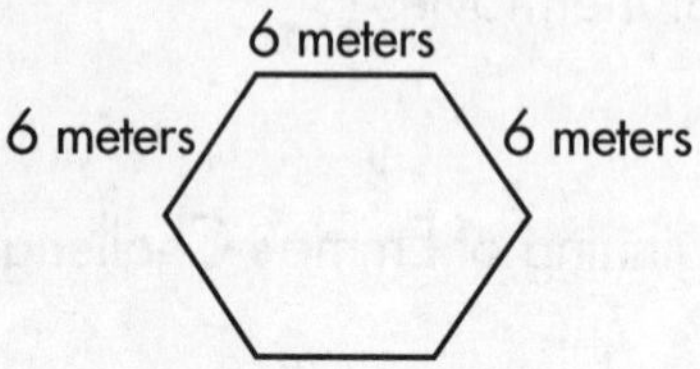

_____ meters

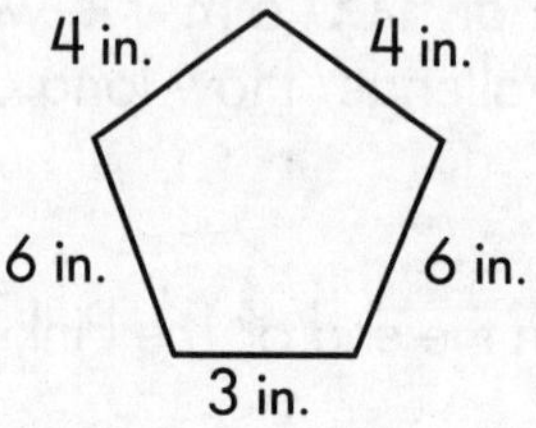

_____ inches

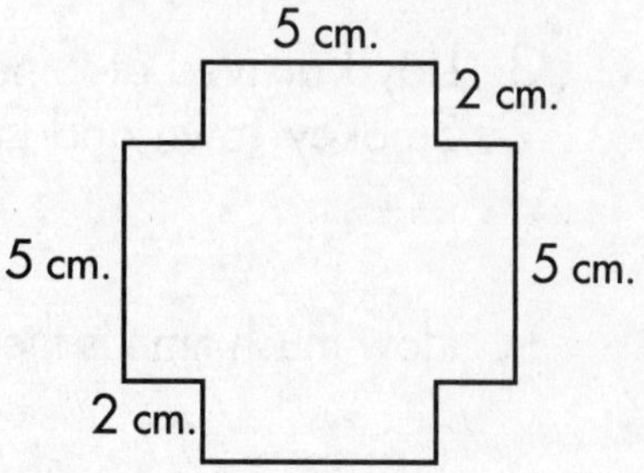

_____ cm.

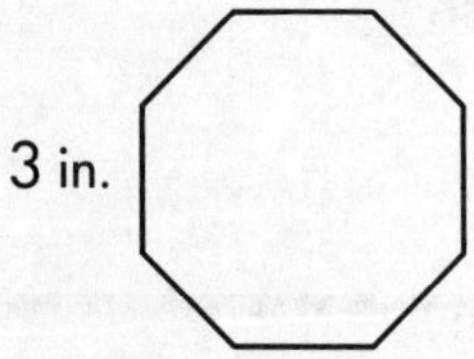

_____ inches

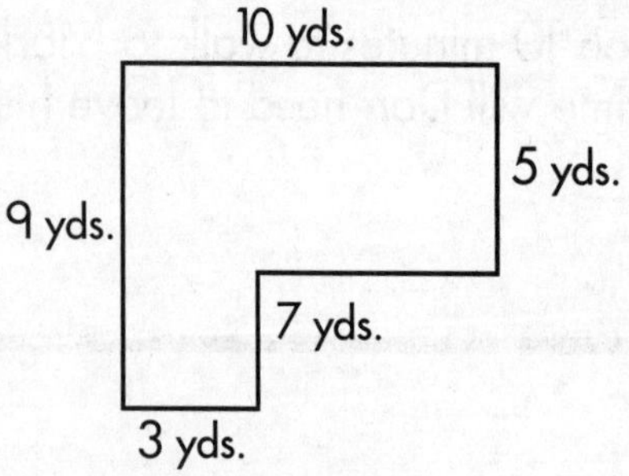

_____ yards

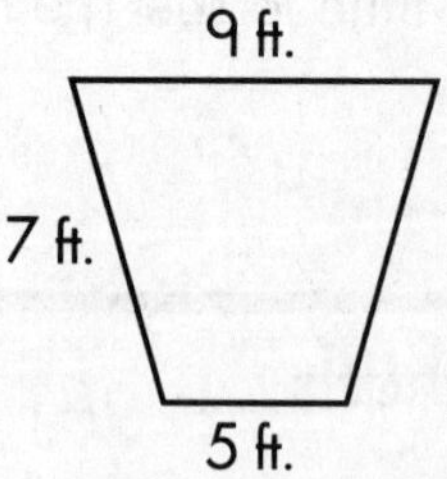

_____ feet

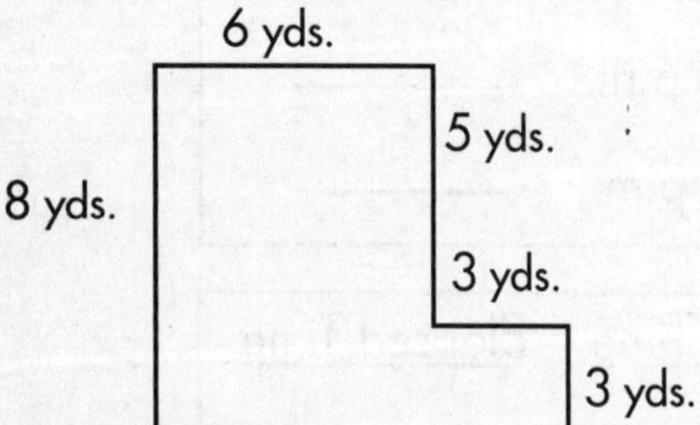

_____ yards

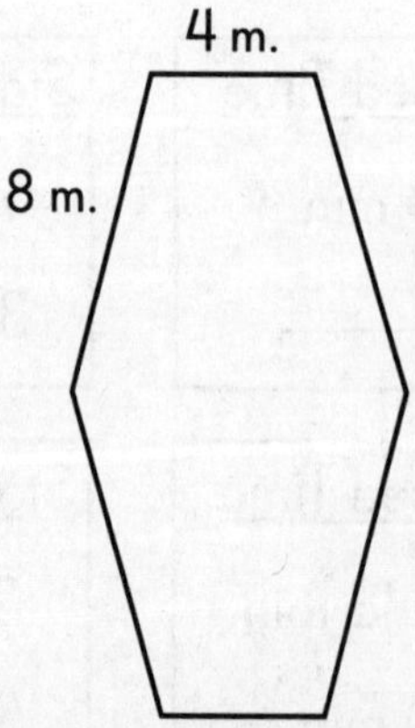

_____ m.

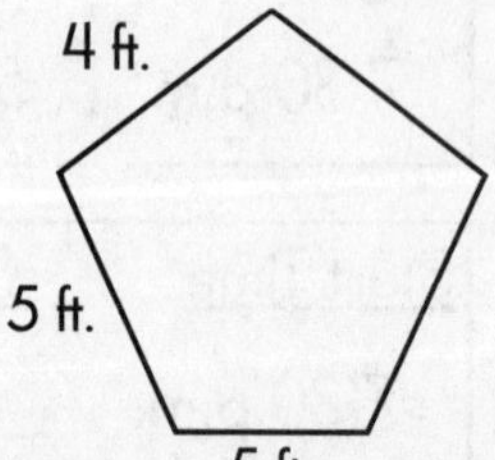

_____ feet

Awesome Amounts of Area

Area is the amount of square units needed (or used) to cover a flat surface.

Area = Length x Width

Find the **area** of each. Write the equation and the answer as square units.

4 in. × 10 in. — 10 x 4 = 40 in. ________

8 ft. × 6 ft. ________

2 cm. × 10 cm. ________

8 m. × 8 m. ________

9 km. × 2 km. ________

3 yds. × 12 yds. ________

13 in. × 3 in. ________

24 yds. × 12 yds. ________

5 m. × 10 m. ________

Amazing Angles

acute right obtuse

Write the name of each angle.

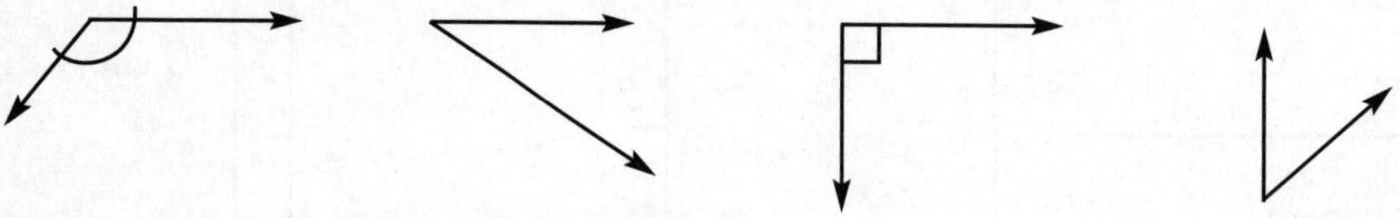

__________ __________ __________ __________

Write the name of the marked angle.

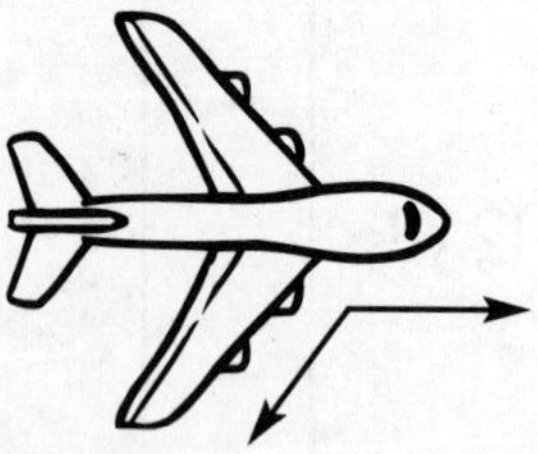

____________________ ____________________

Write the name of the marked angle.

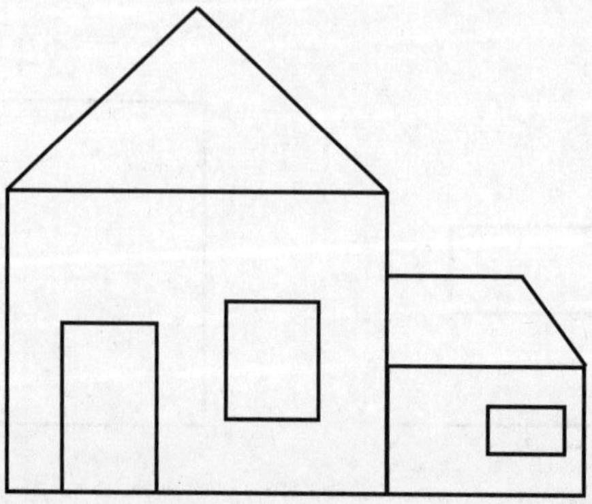

______ acute

______ right

______ obtuse

Measuring Around

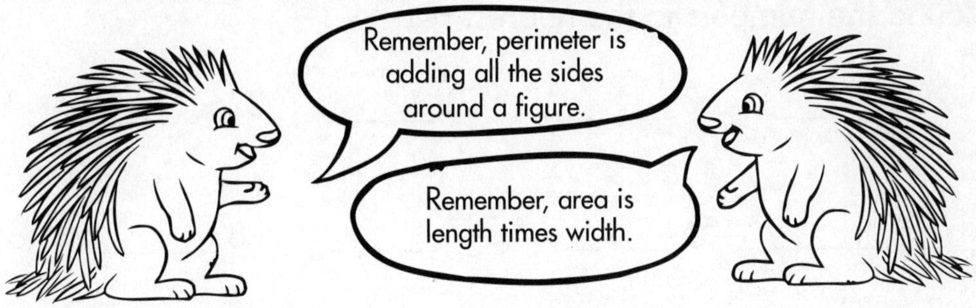

Solve the problems.

1. On Saturday, Kris is running in the 4-mile race at the park. The race goes around the park two times. The park is a square. What is the length of each side?

2. Katie bought a mirror to put in her dollhouse. The perimeter of the mirror is 50 millimeters and the width is 10 millimeters. What is the length?

3. Kyle wants to make a fence for his garden. The garden is 24 feet long and 16 feet wide. How much fence does Kyle need to buy?

4. Stella loves to go to the art museum. Her favorite painting is 25 feet wide and 10 feet tall. What is the area of the painting?

5. Mrs. Smith is buying carpet for a small room in her house. She needs 9 square yards. The carpet costs $5 a square yard. How much will Mrs. Smith pay for the carpet?

6. How many square yards of carpet do you need to cover a floor that is 6 yards long and 4 yards wide?

4 Review

Rounding Numbers

Round the numbers to the nearest **ten**.

248 ______ 63 ______ 71 ______ 326 ______ 104 ______

97 ______ 56 ______ 1,247 ______ 83 ______ 653 ______

45 ______ 132 ______ 87 ______ 49 ______ 99 ______

354 ______ 16 ______ 308 ______ 757 ______ 37 ______

Round the numbers to the nearest **hundred**.

3,743 ______ 12,278 ______ 374 ______ 145 ______

546 ______ 2,453 ______ 98 ______ 4,389 ______

2,614 ______ 194 ______ 7,643 ______ 893 ______

216 ______ 673 ______ 1,783 ______ 574 ______

Round the numbers to the nearest **thousand**.

17,524 ______ 6,429 ______ 3,941 ______ 2,642 ______

4,834 ______ 4,216 ______ 1,823 ______ 9,487 ______

23,573 ______ 6,840 ______ 7,927 ______ 1,431 ______

16,743 ______ 5,327 ______ 9,849 ______ 3,347 ______

Addition Review

Add.

258 + 31	368 + 527	57 + 36	845 + 445	1,684 + 459
245 + 124	681 + 110	1,765 + 4,730	752 + 774	26 + 64
560 + 230	48 + 99	3,287 + 1,721	664 + 201	231 + 421
76 + 23	579 + 457	7,580 + 1,478	305 + 185	1,400 + 2,624
309 + 326	1,486 + 2,006	47 + 32	6,078 + 1,033	1,985 + 2,191

Multiplication Review I

Multiply.

9 x 7	8 x 7	6 x 5	4 x 3	5 x 8	6 x 7
4 x 7	6 x 6	5 x 7	6 x 3	9 x 4	8 x 3
7 x 7	3 x 7	9 x 5	8 x 8	5 x 6	7 x 9
6 x 6	9 x 9	5 x 5	8 x 4	7 x 6	3 x 4
6 x 9	8 x 5	5 x 4	9 x 7	7 x 8	8 x 9
4 x 6	8 x 6	9 x 3	7 x 4	9 x 5	3 x 5

Multiplication Review II

Multiply.

12 x 39	23 x 7	37 x 52	49 x 4	33 x 18	22 x 7
83 x 8	92 x 81	79 x 8	57 x 16	85 x 4	45 x 17
57 x 19	63 x 3	74 x 31	67 x 6	23 x 14	24 x 9
19 x 7	21 x 89	39 x 5	48 x 52	71 x 7	83 x 14
52 x 27	18 x 6	38 x 29	47 x 3	52 x 13	13 x 9
41 x 8	67 x 18	79 x 3	83 x 19	93 x 5	57 x 12

Multiplication Review III

Multiply.

Remember: Multiply the ones place first. Multiply the tens place second.
Then add them together!

613 x 42	459 x 17	931 x 31	372 x 18	492 x 22
785 x 73	412 x 16	396 x 89	137 x 45	209 x 29
917 x 64	406 x 92	381 x 57	710 x 27	118 x 72
814 x 74	926 x 28	231 x 13	174 x 40	349 x 29
905 x 81	714 x 39	817 x 48	273 x 12	384 x 17

Division Review I

Divide.

$2\overline{)4}$	$9\overline{)18}$	$9\overline{)72}$	$9\overline{)0}$	$6\overline{)36}$	$3\overline{)15}$	$4\overline{)20}$
$7\overline{)63}$	$9\overline{)81}$	$2\overline{)14}$	$5\overline{)10}$	$3\overline{)6}$	$2\overline{)2}$	$7\overline{)35}$
$8\overline{)56}$	$7\overline{)49}$	$5\overline{)50}$	$7\overline{)14}$	$5\overline{)25}$	$2\overline{)18}$	$4\overline{)36}$
$8\overline{)72}$	$4\overline{)28}$	$4\overline{)20}$	$5\overline{)30}$	$9\overline{)0}$	$3\overline{)6}$	$9\overline{)81}$
$9\overline{)54}$	$4\overline{)16}$	$9\overline{)63}$	$5\overline{)35}$	$8\overline{)16}$	$9\overline{)45}$	$5\overline{)5}$
$2\overline{)12}$	$7\overline{)14}$	$6\overline{)6}$	$5\overline{)0}$	$7\overline{)49}$	$8\overline{)40}$	$7\overline{)70}$
$3\overline{)12}$	$9\overline{)63}$	$4\overline{)32}$	$3\overline{)21}$	$8\overline{)8}$	$5\overline{)0}$	$2\overline{)14}$

4 Review

Division Review II

Divide.

$7\overline{)91}$	$6\overline{)84}$	$4\overline{)97}$	$5\overline{)75}$	$2\overline{)82}$	$3\overline{)78}$
$3\overline{)72}$	$4\overline{)68}$	$5\overline{)65}$	$2\overline{)72}$	$5\overline{)70}$	$7\overline{)84}$
$6\overline{)93}$	$7\overline{)97}$	$8\overline{)96}$	$3\overline{)81}$	$4\overline{)98}$	$8\overline{)93}$
$2\overline{)98}$	$4\overline{)76}$	$3\overline{)57}$	$5\overline{)92}$	$6\overline{)78}$	$6\overline{)72}$
$2\overline{)88}$	$3\overline{)69}$	$7\overline{)91}$	$6\overline{)83}$	$4\overline{)94}$	$5\overline{)99}$

Division Review III

Divide.

$8\overline{)729}$	$6\overline{)375}$	$7\overline{)575}$	$9\overline{)817}$	$3\overline{)472}$
$4\overline{)159}$	$8\overline{)928}$	$5\overline{)318}$	$7\overline{)287}$	$7\overline{)523}$
$3\overline{)870}$	$9\overline{)760}$	$6\overline{)642}$	$5\overline{)973}$	$9\overline{)387}$
$4\overline{)732}$	$6\overline{)849}$	$8\overline{)417}$	$7\overline{)917}$	$6\overline{)748}$

Let Your Brilliance Shine!

1. Write the numbers using Roman Numerals

66 ______ 47 ______

2.

$$\begin{array}{r} 4{,}793 \\ +\ 349 \\ \hline \end{array} \qquad \begin{array}{r} 3{,}482 \\ -\ 684 \\ \hline \end{array}$$

3. (4 x 7) – 4 ___ 8 + (6 x 5)

O a. ÷ O b. <

O c. = O d. >

4. Round the numbers to the nearest thousand.

7,434 2,921 1,682

_____ _____ _____

5. 4,609.72 - 526.94 = ______

O a. 4,082.73 O b. 4,083.78

O c. 4,082.78 O d. 4,183.78

6. 84 ÷ 9 = ______

O a. 850 O b. 92 r13

O c. 91 r4 O d. 93 r4

7. Write the standard form of three million, forty six thousand, eight hundred three.

8. Write the word form for 5,870,403.

9. Todd's four friends have no sports trading cards of their own. Todd has 246 baseball cards and 134 football cards. He would like to share his cards with his friends. How many cards will Todd and each of his friends receive? Will they all receive the same amount?

10. Priscilla and her three friends like to play with dolls at her house. She has quite a collection and always likes to share evenly. Priscilla has 76 dolls. She wants each person to have the same number of dolls. How many will each person get? Will there be any dolls left over?

11. Kyle feeds his dog Skippy twice a day. Skippy eats a cup of food each time he is fed. How many cups of food will Skippy eat in a four-week period?

Show What You Know!

1. Find the missing number in this pattern.

   176, 171, ____, 161, 156

   ○ a. 169 ○ b. 166

   ○ c. 170 ○ d. 165

2.

   187
   x 92

   904
   x 76

3. I am > 634.
   I am even.
   My digits total 17.
   What number am I?

   ○ a. 619 ○ b. 638 ○ c. 736 ○ d. 566

4. Round the numbers to the nearest hundred.

   3,709 ____ 8,324 ____ 7,641 ____

5. 132.78 + 8,746.23 = ________

6. 9,756 ÷ 8 = ______

7. Write the expanded form of 8,746.

8. 4 hundreds + 11 tens + 7 ones = ________

   ○ a. 417 ○ b. 418

   ○ c. 517 ○ d. 507

9. Jill had saved her babysitting money for several months. She has a total of $89.75 and is going to buy a portable CD player for $37.95 and a CD for 15.99. How much money will Jill have left?

10. Chad sells newspapers. He delivered 378 papers on Monday, 264 papers on Tuesday, and 418 papers on Wednesday. About how many papers has Chad delivered so far this week?

11. Lacey was cleaning her family's closets and found they had a total of 31 pairs of shoes. After talking with the girls at school, she found that Christina's family has 47 pairs of shoes and Emily's small family has 26 pairs of shoes. What method could be used to find how many more pairs of shoes Christina's family has than Emily's family?

    ○ a. Add 31 and 26. ○ b. Subtract 31 from 47.

    ○ c. Add 26 and 31 and subtract the sum from 47. ○ d. Subtract 26 from 47.

Fractions and Decimals

Numbers less than a whole can be written two ways—as a fraction or as a decimal. Rewrite the numbers as fractions or decimals.

$\frac{2}{10}$ = ________	$\frac{40}{100}$ = ________	$\frac{8}{10}$ = ________
.9 = ________	.46 = ________	.79 = ________
$\frac{53}{100}$ = ________	$\frac{3}{10}$ = ________	$\frac{31}{100}$ = ________
56 = ________	.7 = ________	.5 = ________
$\frac{6}{10}$ = ________	$\frac{28}{100}$ = ________	$\frac{1}{10}$ = ________
.83 = ________	.98 = ________	.4 = ________
$\frac{62}{100}$ = ________	.92 = ________	$\frac{43}{100}$ = ________
$\frac{7}{10}$ = ________	.37 = ________	$\frac{18}{100}$ = ________
.51 = ________	$\frac{27}{100}$ = ________	.82 = ________
$\frac{3}{10}$ = ________	.8 = ________	$\frac{19}{100}$ = ________
.21 = ________	$\frac{79}{100}$ = ________	.13 = ________
$\frac{63}{100}$ = ________	.43 = ________	$\frac{74}{100}$ = ________

Mixed Review I

1. Which is the most likely to have the capacity of a gallon?
   - ◯ a. kitchen sink
   - ◯ b. water jug
   - ◯ c. bath tub
   - ◯ d. soda can

2. A bathtub would have the capacity of:
   - ◯ a. 3 gallons
   - ◯ b. 4 pints
   - ◯ c. 50 liters
   - ◯ d. 1 cup

3. Grandma was in the baking mood. She decided to make a cake for each of her five grandchildren. Each cake called for eight ounces of cocoa. How many ounces of cocoa did grandma have to buy?

4. Bill needs his morning coffee. If his coffee pot holds one quart of coffee and he pours himself one cup. How much is in the pot now?

5. An elephant would be measured in what?
   - ◯ a. pounds
   - ◯ b. tons
   - ◯ c. millimeters
   - ◯ d. gallons

6. An encyclopedia would be weighed in what?
   - ◯ a. grams
   - ◯ b. kilograms

   If one encyclopedia weighed 2 ___________, how much would 8 weigh?

7. Tim has a bag of marbles that weighs 18 grams. If Jeff's bag of marbles weighs 27 grams, how much more does Jeff's bag weigh than Tim's?

8. If a new born baby weighs 7 lbs., how many ounces is that?

9. Lacey and Tim competed in a dance marathon. They danced for a total of 4 hours and 28 minutes. How many **minutes** did Lacey and Tim dance?
   - ◯ a. 240 min.
   - ◯ b. 258 min.
   - ◯ c. 158 min.
   - ◯ d. 268 min.

10. Beth checked out a new book from the library. She just couldn't put it down. She read for a total of 1 hour and 57 minutes yesterday and finished it today by reading for 48 minutes. How many total hours and minutes did it take her to read the book?

4 Review

Mixed Review II

Solve the problems.

1. Round 564 to the nearest ten. ○ a. 570 ○ b. 565 ○ c. 560 ○ d. 600	2. Round 5,758 to the nearest hundred. ○ a. 6,000 ○ b. 5,800 ○ c. 5,760 ○ d. 5,700
3. Alora bought eight hair ribbons. Each ribbon was 18 inches long. How many yards of ribbon did Alora purchase? ○ a. 8 yds. 9 in. ○ b. 9 yds. ○ c. 11 yds. 10 in. ○ d. 4 yds.	4. The circus ran out of pennies and nickels to make change so it had to round everything to the nearest \$0.10. What will a \$0.78 item cost? ○ a. \$0.75 ○ b. \$0.80 ○ c. \$1.00 ○ d. \$0.70
5. 578 x 27 693 x 48	6. 278 ÷ 4 = 3,764 ÷ 8 =
7. How much of the pizza has been eaten? Simplify your fraction. 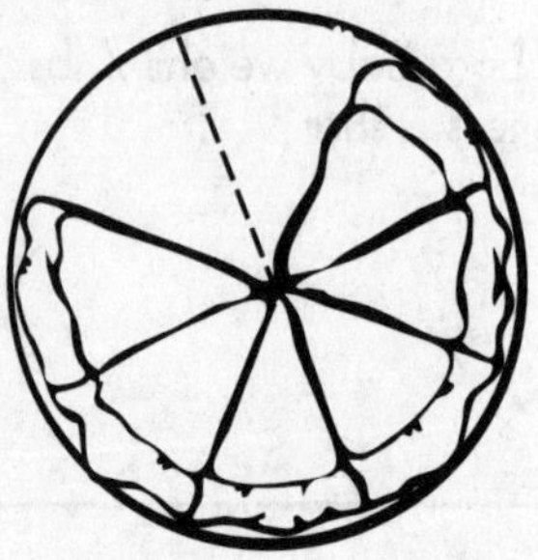	8. Karen is older than David. Mark is older than Karen. Angie is older Mark. Who is the oldest?
9. Connie has a doctor's appointment at 3:30 p.m. She was held up at school and didn't arrive until 4:50 p.m. How late was Connie?	10. Find the greatest common factor for each fraction and simplify. $\frac{16}{64}$ = __ $\frac{9}{54}$ = __ $\frac{25}{45}$ = __

Answer Key

Please take time to review the work your child has completed and remember to praise both success and effort. If your child makes a mistake, let him or her know that mistakes are a part of learning. Then explain the correct answer and how to find it. Taking the time to help your child and an active interest in his or her progress shows that you feel learning is important.

page 1

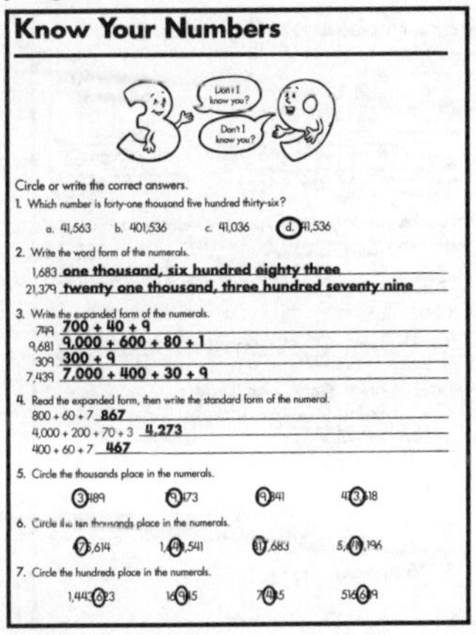

page 2

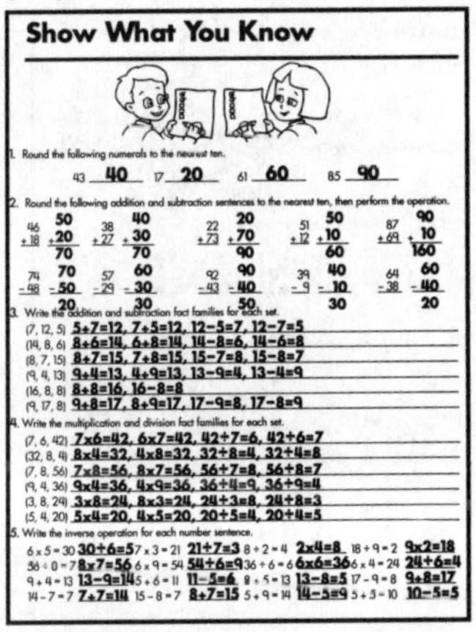

page 3

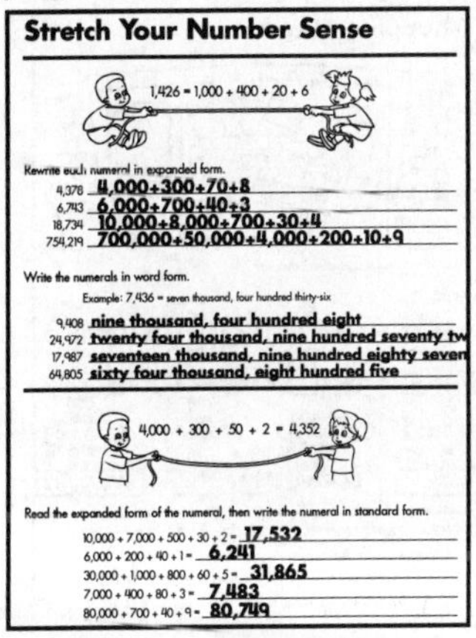

page 4

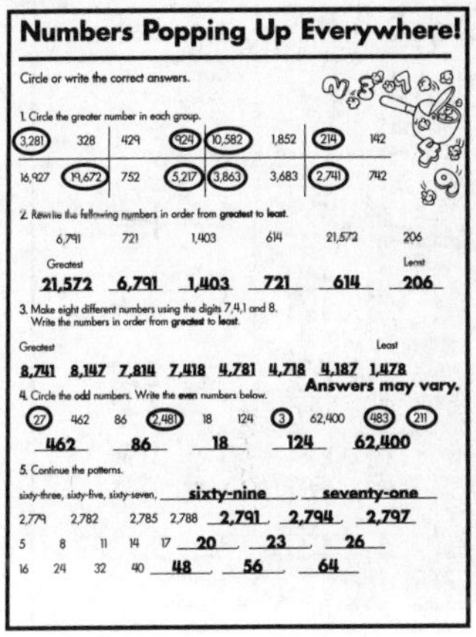

page 5

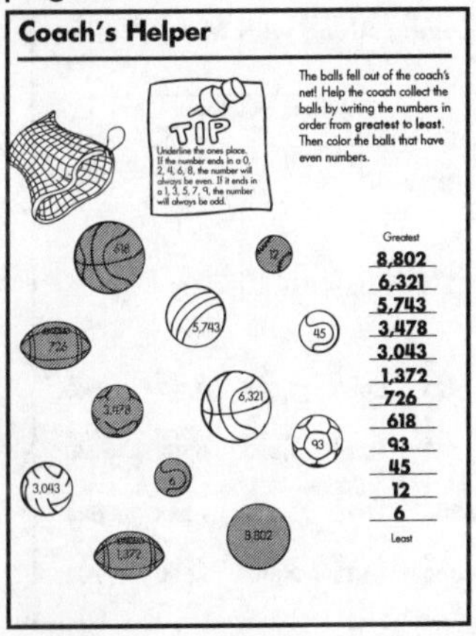

page 6

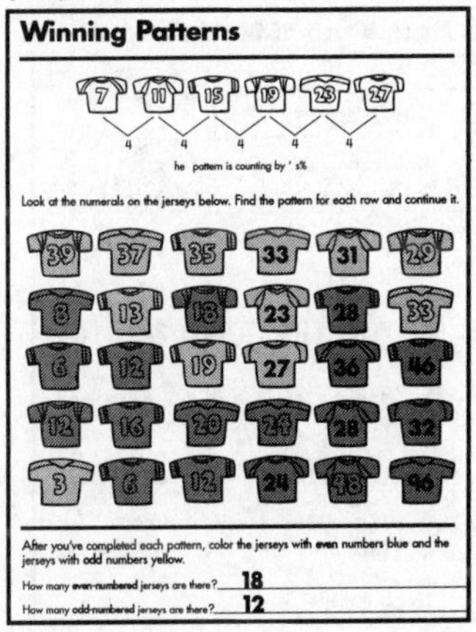

page 7

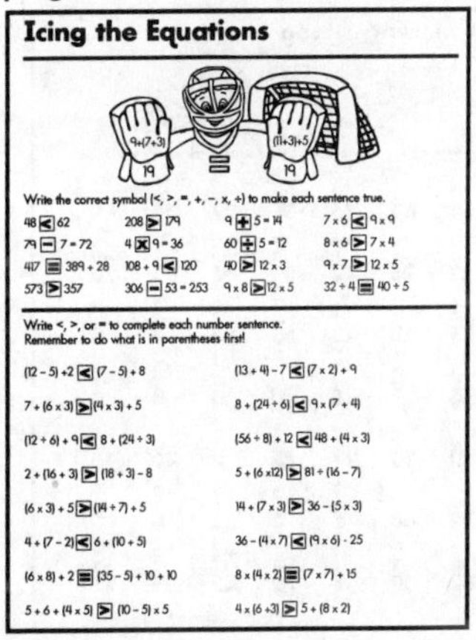

page 8

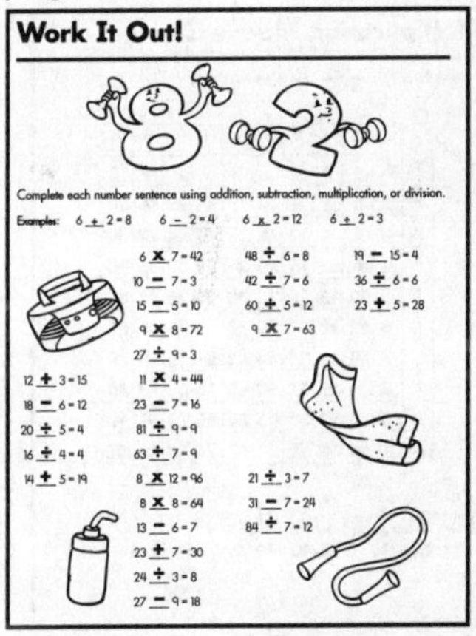

page 9

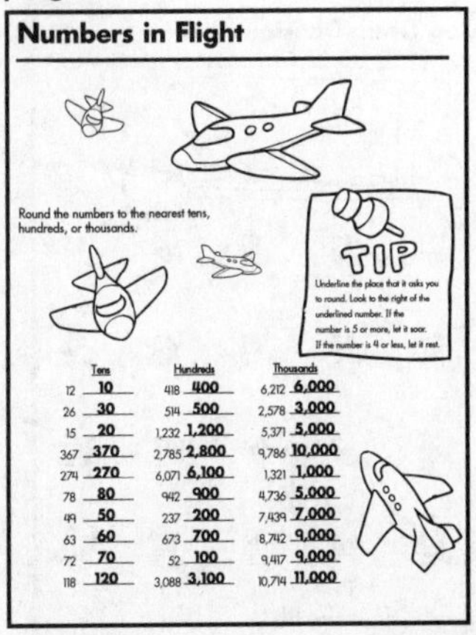

page 10

page 11

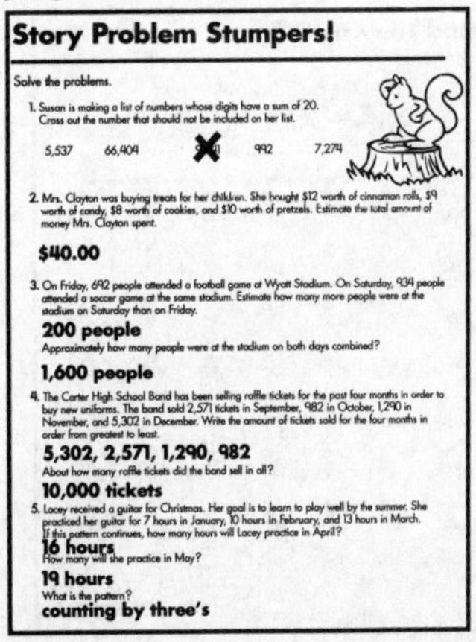

page 12

page 13

A Blockbuster Success!

Add. Circle the sums that are odd numbers.

NOW SHOWING ADDITION SUMS

761, 963, 990
1,465, 1,199, 1,071, 1,246
1,260, 1,536, 1,412, 1,421, 918, 1,243
1,111, 600, 1,018, 1,001, 630, 940
1,182, 1,090, 722, 1,540, 1,003, 612

page 14

Sum Popcorn

Add. Mark an X on the sum if the number is even.

6,867, 9,763, 9,800, 11,096, 3,326
8,496, 8,963, 13,083, 7,410, 5,857
4,360, 4,501, 6,194, 5,253, 6,296
5,753, 10,140, 11,712, 7,191, 15,202
7,902, 8,101, 4,025, 4,861, 9,165

page 15

Falling Amounts

Subtract.

601, 231, 403, 140, 433
220, 230, 233, 421, 231
431, 724, 221, 12, 313
203, 532, 152, 241, 515
512, 212, 820, 501, 343

page 16

Gardening Troubles

Why was the farmer looking for his keys in the garden?

Solve the problems. Then write the letters below to answer the riddle.

T 29, Y 9, H 17, S 85, I 6
T 38, D 46, H 67, N 8, E 48
O 24, U 28, R 14, E 48, I 56
W 16, H 5, A 25, P 12, N 13
W 49, G 19

HE WAS HOPING THEY'D TURNIP

page 17

A Garden of Good Subtraction

Solve the problems. Check your subtraction with addition!

1. 3,712 − 1,895 = 1,817; 1,817 + 1,895 = 3,712
2. 7,406 − 3,677 = 3,729; 3,729 + 3,677 = 7,406
3. 3,413 − 1,798 = 1,615; 1,615 + 1,798 = 3,413
4. 5,935 − 2,329 = 3,606; 3,606 + 2,329 = 5,935
5. 3,009 − 1,998 = 1,011; 1,011 + 1,998 = 3,009
6. 6,187 − 2,789 = 3,398; 3,398 + 2,789 = 6,187
7. 4,108 − 2,299 = 1,809; 1,809 + 2,299 = 4,108
8. 2,112 − 998 = 1,114; 1,114 + 998 = 2,112

Round the answers to the subtraction problems to the nearest thousand.

1. 2,000 2. 4,000 3. 2,000 4. 4,000
5. 1,000 6. 3,000 7. 2,000 8. 1,000

page 18

Shopping Success

Add. Don't forget to line up your decimals!

$165.77, $40.64, $563.12, $449.48
$578.50, $787.23, $794.68, $900.63
$9,483.30, $2,886.90, $7,173.41, $3,186.69
$12,524.41, $7,110.02, $11,013.99, $15,203.12

After you've solved the problems, do the following. (Round to the nearest thousand.)

1. Circle the sums that can be rounded between $1,000 and $5,000.
2. Mark an X on the sums that can be rounded between $6,000 and $10,000.
3. Draw a box around the sums that can be rounded between $11,000 and $15,000.

page 19

Fruitful Fun with Decimals

4.927 − 1.237 = 3.690; 3.690 + 1.237 = 4.927

Remember to line up your decimals!

Subtract. Then use addition to check your answers.

1.07, 1.23 | 3.34, 6.58 | 70.81, 92.36
1.16, 2.36 | 4.25, 5.03 | 6.09, 16.25
68.45, 85.21 | 27.76, 52.89 | .45, 17.23
13.82, 18.56 | 6.96, 23.79 | 27.49, 43.28

page 20

Story Problems...Downloading

Solve the problems.

1. Blaine saw a computer for $475.00 and a printer for $135.00. He decided this was a good deal and just what he needed. In order to buy the computer, Blaine worked each week for three months. He earned $136.00 in March, $231.00 in April, and $179.00 in May. Has Blaine earned enough money to buy the computer and printer? If so, how much will he have left after making the purchase?

   No, he doesn't have enough money to buy it.

2. Lilly was playing a computer game about traveling across the United States. The object of this game is to keep track of the miles traveled. In the first round of the game, Lilly traveled 413 miles. In the second round, she encountered many problems and traveled only 281 miles. She had a successful third round and traveled 674 miles. What is the approximate total number of miles that Lilly traveled in the game?

   1,400 miles

3. Several of the students in Mrs. Dee's computer class were trying to decide who was the oldest. Carter is younger than Leigh, but older than Kendra. Mark is between Kendra and Carter. List the students from oldest to youngest.

   Leigh, Carter Mark, and Kendra

4. The technology students have been studying the rise in population in their city over the past ten years in order to produce graphs. In the first three years, the population increased by 3,716 people. In the next four years, the population went up again by 4,119 people. Finally, in the past three years, it increased by 9,658 people. What is the total number of people the population has increased by over the past ten years?

   17,493 people

5. The Cunningham High School Technology Team logs the amount of minutes they spend on the computer each month. In September, they logged 3,107 minutes. In October, they were busy with projects and logged a total of 8,983 minutes for the month. How many more minutes did the technology team log in October than in September?

   5,876 minutes

page 21

Multiplication Madness

Complete the multiplication table. Do you see the pattern?

x	1	2	3	4	5	6	7	8	9	10
1	1	2	3	4	5	6	7	8	9	10
2	2	4	6	8	10	12	14	16	18	20
3	3	6	9	12	15	18	21	24	27	30
4	4	8	12	16	20	24	28	32	36	40
5	5	10	15	20	25	30	35	40	45	50
6	6	12	18	24	30	36	42	48	54	60
7	7	14	21	28	35	42	49	56	63	70
8	8	16	24	32	40	48	56	64	72	80
9	9	18	27	36	45	54	63	72	81	90
10	10	20	30	40	50	60	70	80	90	100

A fact family looks like this: 6 x 7 = 42, 7 x 6 = 42, 42 ÷ 6 = 7, 42 ÷ 7 = 6
Create a fact family using the numbers 2, 5, and 10.

2x5=10 5x2=10 10÷2=5 10÷5=2

page 22

Speeding Along

Solve the problems as fast as you can. Time yourself or ask someone to time you.

24, 63, 15, 56, 27, 30, 9
12, 36, 72, 24, 36, 35, 20
45, 64, 42, 63, 24, 4, 6
3, 0, 48, 21, 16, 9, 21
81, 20, 27, 14, 8, 40, 16
49, 18, 6, 0, 32, 0, 0
63, 10, 18, 72, 42, 14, 27

Time: ______ Missed ______ out of 49

page 23

A Fresh Batch of Multiplication

Step 1: 24 x 4 — Multiply the ones place first, 4 x 4 = 16. Write the 6 in the ones place. Write the 1 ten above so you remember it.

Step 2: 24 x 4 = 96 — Now, multiply the tens place. 2 tens x 4 = 8 tens. Add the 1 ten to make it 9 tens.

Multiply.

96, 207, 114, 42, 204, 60
165, 172, 58, 180, 85, 280
54, 78, 224, 84, 378, 130
75, 136, 54, 64, 154, 132

page 24

Moving Along with Multiplication

High-Flying Multiplication

A. 23 x 4 = 92 (multiply the ones first)
B. 23 x 4 = 92 (don't forget to add the ten you carried)
C. 23 x 14: 92, 230 (use a 0 to hold the one's place)
D. 23 x 14: 92 + 230 = 322 (add)

Multiply.

924, 2,064, 1,508, 1,197, 840
912, 1,224, 1,022, 4,914, 391
2,808, 1,428, 812, 1,288, 648
1,800, 1,530, 2,397, 3,690, 702

page 25

Fast Forward with Multiplication

A. 343 x 152 = 686 — Multiply the ones.
B. 343 x 152: 686, 1,7150 — Multiply the tens.
C. 343 x 152: 686 + 17150 + 17,1500 = 17,836 — Then add it all up!

Multiply.

9,384, 29,636, 41,715, 24,389, 50,962
30,447, 48,034, 11,888, 4,788, 3,585
5,810, 69,402, 3,667, 11,155, 5,406
10,296, 5,412, 15,600, 66,748, 16,940

page 26

And They're Off

Solve the problems as fast as you can. Time yourself or ask someone to time you.

8, 4, 7, 3, 9, 6, 7
5, 0, 2, 9, 7, 5, 7
2, 1, 3, 2, 4, 9, 2
0, 2, 2, 9, 7, 8, 8
3, 8, 8, 5, 5, 1, 5
1, 5, 3, 5, 3, 7, 8
7, 3, 0, 5, 4, 6, 6

Time: ______ Missed ______ out of 49

A winner knows that division is the inverse of multiplication.

page 27

Leaping Lizards Long Division

Divide to find the quotient. Watch out for remainders!

7, 4, 9r3, 5r7, 6r8, 7r2
7, 8r5, 7r2, 6, 2, 7r2
9r7, 9r1, 5, 7r4, 5, 8
8, 9r6, 5, 8r3, 5, 9

page 28

Dog Gone Division

Divide.

131, 72, 91, 40, 65
28, 47, 61, 80, 92
31, 52, 63, 107, 251
85, 76, 18, 82, 126

page 29

Take the Challenge!

Divide.

217 (7)1,519); 547r2 (8)4,378); 644r2 (4)2,578); 925r2 (9)8,327); 951r5 (8)7,613)

581r1 (6)3,487); 315 (5)1,575); 1,393 (3)4,179); 323 (6)1,938); 837r1 (2)1,675)

368r1 (7)2,577); 312 (8)2,496); 534r3 (5)2,673); 431r1 (4)1,725); 891r1 (3)2,674)

page 30

Think About It

Solve the problems. Show your work!

1. Kelli bought a new photo album to display her vacation pictures. Each page of the album displays six photos. There are a total of 143 pages in the book. How many photos can the album hold?

858 photos

If Kelli has 964 photos, how many more pages does she need?

18 pages

2. Farmer Joe has many chickens on his farm. Every week he collects and fills 238 cartons of eggs to take to the market. Each carton can hold 12 eggs. What is the total number of eggs that Farmer Joe collects in one week?

2,856 eggs

3. Sophie enjoys reading. Over the past week and a half, Sophie has read seven books with a total of 966 pages. If all seven books have the same number of pages, which number sentence can be used to find the number of pages in each book?

a. 966 + 7 = ___ b. 966 x 7 = ___ c. 966 ÷ 7 = ✓ d. 966 – 7 = ___

How many pages were in each book?

138 pages

4. Kendra's father is a carpenter. Last week he repaired Mrs. Gibson's deck. He worked for six hours a day for two days until the job was complete. Kendra's father then billed Mrs. Gibson for $45.00 an hour. What was the total amount that Mrs. Gibson had to pay?

$540.00

5. Jesse had 93 miniature racecars and 87 semi-trucks. The toy tracks that he has will make up ten different roads. Jesse wants to put an equal number of vehicles on each road. How many vehicles can he put on each road?

18 vehicles

page 31

Delicious Fractions

Color the correct amount.

$=\frac{3}{4}$, $=\frac{3}{8}$, $=\frac{4}{8}$, $=\frac{3}{9}$, $=\frac{4}{6}$

Draw a picture and color part of it to show the fraction.

$\frac{7}{8}$, $\frac{4}{10}$, $\frac{3}{5}$, $\frac{2}{5}$, $\frac{2}{7}$, $\frac{5}{6}$

page 32

Fraction Double Take

Write the equivalent fraction.

Fractions that name the same amount are called equivalent fractions!

$\frac{1}{2}=\frac{2}{4}$, $\frac{1}{4}=\frac{2}{8}$, $\frac{2}{3}=\frac{4}{6}$, $\frac{1}{3}=\frac{3}{9}$, $\frac{1}{3}=\frac{2}{6}$, $\frac{1}{2}=\frac{6}{12}$, $\frac{1}{2}=\frac{4}{8}$, $\frac{1}{5}=\frac{2}{10}$, $\frac{9}{15}=\frac{3}{5}$

page 33

Fraction Review I

Shade the correct number triangles to show the fraction. Then write the number that you shaded.

$\frac{1}{3}$ of 6 = **2**, $\frac{1}{5}$ of 10 = **2**, $\frac{1}{3}$ of 9 = **3**

$\frac{1}{2}$ of 4 = **2**, $\frac{1}{4}$ of 12 = **3**, $\frac{2}{3}$ of 9 = **6**

Draw the correct number of circles and shade the number of parts shown. Then write the fraction for the shaded area.

6 circles, 3 parts = **3/6**	8 circles, 2 parts = **2/8**	10 circles, 5 parts = **5/10**
12 circles, 4 parts = **4/12**	15 circles, 3 parts = **3/15**	6 circles, 2 parts = **2/6**

page 34

Adding it Up

Adding fractions are easy when the denominations are the same.

$\frac{1}{6}+\frac{3}{6}=\frac{4}{6}$ → numerator, → denominator

Add.

$\frac{2}{6}+\frac{4}{6}=\frac{6}{6}=1$	$\frac{1}{5}+\frac{1}{5}=\frac{2}{5}$	$\frac{4}{16}+\frac{7}{16}=\frac{11}{16}$
$\frac{6}{10}+\frac{3}{10}=\frac{9}{10}$	$\frac{1}{9}+\frac{6}{9}=\frac{7}{9}$	$\frac{5}{8}+\frac{2}{8}=\frac{7}{8}$
$\frac{5}{9}+\frac{1}{9}=\frac{6}{9}$	$\frac{2}{7}+\frac{1}{7}=\frac{3}{7}$	$\frac{2}{6}+\frac{3}{6}=\frac{5}{6}$
$\frac{2}{10}+\frac{7}{10}=\frac{9}{10}$	$\frac{1}{12}+\frac{3}{12}=\frac{4}{12}$	$\frac{3}{9}+\frac{4}{9}=\frac{7}{9}$
$\frac{3}{8}+\frac{5}{8}=\frac{8}{8}=1$	$\frac{3}{5}+\frac{1}{5}=\frac{4}{5}$	$\frac{5}{12}+\frac{6}{12}=\frac{11}{12}$
$\frac{7}{16}+\frac{4}{16}=\frac{11}{16}$	$\frac{5}{10}+\frac{3}{10}=\frac{8}{10}$	$\frac{6}{14}+\frac{1}{14}=\frac{7}{14}$
$\frac{4}{8}+\frac{2}{8}=\frac{6}{8}$	$\frac{3}{15}+\frac{7}{15}=\frac{10}{15}$	$\frac{3}{12}+\frac{7}{12}=\frac{10}{12}$

page 35

Fraction Review II

Solve the fraction problems. Remember to watch your signs.

$\frac{1}{6}+\frac{2}{6}=\frac{3}{6}$	$\frac{3}{5}-\frac{1}{5}=\frac{2}{5}$	$\frac{5}{12}+\frac{6}{12}=\frac{11}{12}$
$\frac{5}{9}+\frac{1}{9}=\frac{6}{9}$	$\frac{7}{10}+\frac{2}{10}=\frac{9}{10}$	$\frac{6}{12}-\frac{2}{12}=\frac{4}{12}$
$\frac{7}{9}-\frac{5}{9}=\frac{2}{9}$	$\frac{9}{10}-\frac{5}{10}=\frac{4}{10}$	$\frac{2}{3}-\frac{1}{3}=\frac{1}{3}$
$\frac{7}{8}-\frac{3}{8}=\frac{4}{8}$	$\frac{3}{7}+\frac{1}{7}=\frac{4}{7}$	$\frac{5}{8}+\frac{2}{8}=\frac{7}{8}$
$\frac{4}{16}+\frac{4}{16}=\frac{8}{16}$	$\frac{8}{12}+\frac{2}{12}=\frac{10}{12}$	$\frac{9}{12}-\frac{4}{12}=\frac{5}{12}$
$\frac{7}{10}-\frac{4}{10}=\frac{3}{10}$	$\frac{4}{9}+\frac{4}{9}=\frac{8}{9}$	$\frac{8}{16}-\frac{4}{16}=\frac{4}{16}$
$\frac{5}{15}+\frac{10}{15}=\frac{15}{15}=1$	$\frac{7}{16}-\frac{5}{16}=\frac{2}{16}$	$\frac{9}{12}+\frac{2}{12}=\frac{11}{12}$

page 36

Fun with Fractions

Finding the greatest common factors for both numbers can be easy!

Simplify these fractions!

$\frac{8}{32}$ List all the factors that equal the numerator! (1,2,4,8)

List all the factors that equal the denominator! (1,2,4,8,32)

Now, circle the greatest common factor!

Write down the common factors for the numerators and denominators below. Circle the greatest common factor for each fraction.

$\frac{6}{18}$: 1,2,3,(6) / 1,2,3,(6),9,18; $\frac{6}{24}$: 1,2,3,(6) / 1,2,3,4,(6),8,12,24; $\frac{9}{36}$: 1,3,(9) / 1,2,3,4,6,(9),12,18,36; $\frac{7}{42}$: 1,(7) / 1,2,3,6,(7),14,21,42

$\frac{9}{81}$: 1,3,(9) / 1,3,(9),27,81; $\frac{8}{48}$: 1,2,4,(8) / 1,2,3,4,6,(8),12,16,24,48; $\frac{12}{36}$: 1,2,3,4,6,(12) / 1,2,3,4,6,9,(12),18,36; $\frac{14}{28}$: 1,2,7,(14) / 1,2,4,7,(14),28

Example: $\frac{3}{6}\div\frac{3}{3}=\frac{1}{2}$ 1st – Find the greatest common factor of the numerator and denominator. 2nd – Divide both the numerator and denominator by that number.

Congratulations! You've just simplified that fraction!

Simplify the fractions.

$\frac{4}{12}=\frac{1}{3}$	$\frac{5}{25}=\frac{1}{5}$	$\frac{7}{28}=\frac{1}{4}$	$\frac{6}{48}=\frac{1}{8}$	$\frac{7}{63}=\frac{1}{9}$
$\frac{12}{24}=\frac{1}{2}$	$\frac{14}{21}=\frac{2}{3}$	$\frac{4}{32}=\frac{1}{8}$	$\frac{7}{63}=\frac{1}{9}$	$\frac{9}{36}=\frac{1}{4}$
$\frac{3}{18}=\frac{1}{6}$	$\frac{9}{27}=\frac{1}{3}$	$\frac{6}{12}=\frac{1}{2}$	$\frac{12}{48}=\frac{1}{4}$	$\frac{9}{12}=\frac{3}{4}$
$\frac{5}{20}=\frac{1}{4}$	$\frac{8}{16}=\frac{1}{2}$	$\frac{7}{21}=\frac{1}{3}$	$\frac{16}{48}=\frac{1}{3}$	$\frac{8}{12}=\frac{2}{3}$

page 37

Different, but the SAME!

Write the fraction and mixed numeral for each.

$\frac{5}{2}$ $2\frac{1}{2}$; $\frac{8}{3}$ $2\frac{2}{3}$; $\frac{21}{6}$ $3\frac{3}{6}$; $\frac{11}{4}$ $2\frac{3}{4}$; $\frac{7}{2}$ $3\frac{1}{2}$; $\frac{14}{4}$ $3\frac{2}{4}$; $\frac{5}{2}$ $2\frac{1}{2}$; $\frac{5}{8}$ no mixed number; $\frac{28}{6}$ $4\frac{4}{6}$; $\frac{11}{3}$ $3\frac{2}{3}$

page 38

That's Top Heavy

An improper fraction is a top heavy fraction.

The numerator 32 is larger than the denominator 9 so it's top heavy!

Here's how to convert a mixed number to an improper fraction.

$3\frac{5}{9}$ Step 1: Take the whole number (3). Step 2: Multiply it by the denominator (9). 3 x 9 = 27 Step 3: Add the numerator (5). 27 + 5 = 32 Step 4: Place the total over the denominator (9). $\frac{32}{9}$

Write the mixed number as an improper fraction.

$2\frac{3}{4}=\frac{11}{4}$	$6\frac{4}{5}=\frac{34}{5}$	$8\frac{4}{7}=\frac{60}{7}$
$4\frac{5}{8}=\frac{37}{8}$	$7\frac{3}{7}=\frac{52}{7}$	$5\frac{2}{8}=\frac{42}{8}$
$8\frac{3}{4}=\frac{35}{4}$	$5\frac{1}{2}=\frac{11}{2}$	$3\frac{4}{8}=\frac{28}{8}$
$3\frac{2}{9}=\frac{29}{9}$	$7\frac{5}{9}=\frac{68}{9}$	$7\frac{2}{6}=\frac{44}{6}$
$2\frac{1}{4}=\frac{9}{4}$	$2\frac{3}{7}=\frac{17}{7}$	$3\frac{5}{7}=\frac{26}{7}$
$5\frac{3}{8}=\frac{43}{8}$	$4\frac{1}{6}=\frac{25}{6}$	$1\frac{7}{9}=\frac{16}{9}$
$5\frac{2}{8}=\frac{42}{8}$	$6\frac{3}{5}=\frac{33}{5}$	$8\frac{3}{5}=\frac{43}{5}$
$1\frac{5}{9}=\frac{14}{9}$	$8\frac{4}{9}=\frac{76}{9}$	$2\frac{7}{8}=\frac{23}{8}$

page 39

What's the Value?

Hundreds Tens Ones • Tenths Hundredths — 2 = $\frac{2}{10}$

A decimal is a number that uses place value and a decimal to show value less than a whole (or one).

A fraction does the same thing. So fractions and decimals mean the same thing. They are just written a little differently.

This whole is divided into tenths. $\frac{2}{10}$ = .2 — .26 = $\frac{26}{100}$ This whole is divided into hundredths.

Write the fraction and the decimal number for each.

$\frac{24}{100}$ = .24	$\frac{3}{10}$ = .30 or .3
$\frac{7}{10}$ = .70 or.7	$\frac{42}{100}$ = .42
$\frac{52}{100}$ = .52	$\frac{4}{10}$ = .40 or .4
$\frac{5}{10}$ = .50 or .5	$\frac{19}{100}$ = .19

page 40

Changing Units

The Golden Rule

When you change larger units to smaller units, you multiply. Example: 4 yards x 3 feet = 12 feet

When you change smaller units to larger units, you divide. Example: 36 inches ÷ 12 feet = 3 feet

Convert each unit of measure.

Customary Units for Linear Measures: 12 inches = 1 foot; 3 feet = 1 yard; 5,280 feet = 1 mile; 1,760 yards = 1 mile

9 feet = **3** yards	2 miles **10,560** feet	12 inches = **1** foot
36 inches = **1** yards	9 yards = **27** feet	
48 inches = **4** feet	60 inches = **5** feet	
7 feet = **84** inches	96 inches = **8** feet	9 feet = **108** inches
36 feet = **12** yards	12 yards = **432** inches	3 miles = **5,280** yards
3,520 yards = **2** miles	144 inches = **12** feet	18 yards = **648** inches
5 yards = **15** feet	5 miles **26,400** feet	46 feet = **552** inches
6 feet = **2** yards	12 feet = **144** inches	48 feet = **16** yards
3 miles **15,840** feet	9 miles **15,840** yards	72 inches = **6** feet
14 feet = **168** inches	2 miles **10,560** feet	24 feet = **8** yards
6 yards = **216** inches	30 yards = **90** feet	84 inches = **7** feet
21 feet = **7** yards	10 yards = **360** inches	4 miles **21,120** feet

If fencing is $2.00 per foot, how much would it cost to fence a dog run with a 36-yard perimeter for Brutus to have fun in?

36x3=108 feet 108x$2=$216.00

page 41

The Rule of Thumb

Remember to multiply when you change larger units to smaller units and to divide when you change smaller units to larger units.

Customary Units for Measuring Liquids: 1 pint = 2 cups c.; 1 quart = 2 pints pt.; 1 gallon = 4 quarts qt.

Customary Units for Measuring Weight: 16 ounces oz. = 1 pound lb.; 2000 lbs = 1 ton T.

Circle the more reasonable measurement.

300 T. / (300 lbs.); (4 oz.) / 4 lbs.; 14 oz. / (14 lbs.); (10 lbs.) / 10 T.; (15 T.) / 15 lbs.; 1 lb. / (1 oz.); (15 lb.) / 15 oz.

Convert each unit of measure.

8 cups = **2** qt.	2 lb = **32** oz.	3 pt = **6** c.
3 gal = **12** qt.	64 oz = **4** lb.	2 gal = **16** pt.
1 qt = **4** c.	4 T **8,000** lb.	3 qt = **12** c.
12 pt = **24** c.	3 lbs = **48** oz.	8 lb = **128** oz.
3 qt = **12** c.	6 pt = **12** c.	5 gal = **20** qt.

Tony needs four cups of cream for a pie. The store sells cream in one-pint containers. How many pints should Tony buy? **2 pints**

page 42

Where in the World

Customary Units For Measuring Time: 60 seconds = 1 minute; 60 minutes = 1 hour; 24 hours = 1 day

Solve the problems.

1. Clay spends seven hours each day at school. He goes to school Monday through Friday. About how many hours does Clay spend at school in one week?

about 35 hours

2. Craig's guitar lessons were two hours long. If his lesson ended at 6:15, what time did it begin?

4:15

3. Cheryl spent the day cleaning. It took her 25 minutes to vacuum, 18 minutes to dust, and 90 minutes to do the laundry. How many minutes did she spend cleaning?

133 minutes

How many hours?

2 hours and 13 minutes

4. Barbara exercised for 24 minutes. Then she watched television for 40 minutes. Did the two activities combined take more or less than an hour?

more than an hour

5. Abbey sleeps for ten hours. Then she takes her friends to the mall for six hours and the water park for seven hours. Finally, Abbey spends two hours eating meals and helping her mom around the house. Will she be able to do everything in one day? Explain your answer.

No. 1 day=24 hours 10+6+7+2=25 hours

Challenge yourself! Create a list of things that you do that takes a second, minute, hour, or day.

Answers will vary.

page 43

Elapsed Time

Saturday Movie Times at Cinema Town: 10:00 a.m. Smokey Town; 11:45 a.m. The Pink Cat; 12:15 p.m. Julie's Wish; 3:30 p.m. Emma's Challenge

What time does it start?

1. All the movies last 2 hours and 10 minutes. At what time will each movie end?

Smokey Town-12:10p.m., The Pink Cat-1:55p.m, Julie's Wish-2:25p.m., Emma's Challenge-5:40p.m.

2. If Elizabeth had to walk home after the 3:30 p.m. showing of Emma's Challenge and it took her 20 minutes to walk home, at what time would she get home?

6:00p.m.

3. Lloyd arrived at Cinema Town at 9:00 a.m. He was able to stay long enough to watch Smokey Town and Emma's Challenge. How long did Lloyd stay at the movies?

Lloyd has to wait until 10:00a.m. for Smokey Town to start and Emma's Challange is over at 5:40p.m., so he was at the moveis for 8hours and 40minutes.

4. How much time is there between the end of The Pink Cat and the beginning of Emma's Challenge?

1 hour and 35 minutes

5. Don and Mark are going to the movies. The movie theater is closer to Mark's house and it takes 15 minutes to get there. If it takes Don 10 minutes to walk to Mark's house and they want to leave in time to see The Pink Cat what time will Don need to leave his house?

11:45 (25 minutes before the movie starts)

Complete the charts.

Start Time	End Time	Elapsed Time
1:15 a.m.	**2:05a.m.**	50 min.
7:30 a.m.	5:25 p.m.	**9 hrs. 55 min.**

Start Time	End Time	Elapsed Time
1:30 p.m.	2:40 p.m.	**1 hr. 10 min.**
3:45 p.m.	5:15 p.m.	**1 hr. 30 min.**

Start Time	End Time	Elapsed Time
7:30 p.m.	**8:43p.m.**	1 hr. 13 min.
8:15 p.m.	**8:55p.m.**	40 min.

Start Time	End Time	Elapsed Time
2:15 p.m.	7:30 p.m.	**5 hrs. 15 min.**
5:45 p.m.	**7:05p.m.**	1 hr. 20 min.

page 44

Perimeter, It's What's Around You!

Perimeter is the distance around a figure. To find the perimeter of a shape or figure, add all the sides.

Hmm...?

4 ft. + 4 ft. = 8 ft. and 6 ft. + 6 ft. = 12 ft. OR 4 ft. x 2 sides = 8 ft. and 6 ft. x 2 sides = 12 ft. 8 ft. + 12 ft. = 20 ft. in perimeter

Find the perimeter of each shape.

36 meters; **23** inches; **36** cm.; **24** inches; **38** yards; **28** feet; **34** yards; **40** m.; **23** feet

page 45

Awesome Amounts of Area

Area is the amount of square units needed (or used) to cover a flat surface.

Area = Length x Width

Find the area of each. Write the equation and the answer.

- 4 in. × 10 in.: 10 x 4 = **40 in.**
- 8 ft. × 6 ft.: **48 ft.**
- 2 cm. × 10 cm.: **20 cm**
- 8 m. × 8 m.: **64 m.**
- 9 km. × 2 km.: **18 km.**
- 3 yds. × 12 yds.: **36 yds.**
- 13 in. × 3 in.: **39 in.**
- 24 yds. × 12 yds.: **288 yds.**
- 5 m. × 10 m.: **50 m.**

page 46

Amazing Angles

acute right obtuse

Write the name of each angle.

obtuse **acute** **right** **acute**

Write the name of the marked angle.

obtuse **right**

How many angles can you find in the house?

4 acute **21** right **1** obtuse

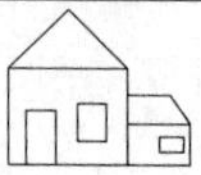

page 47

Measuring Around

Solve the problems.

1. On Saturday, Kris is running in the 4-mile race at the park. The race goes around the park two times. The park is a square. What is the length of each side?
   $\frac{1}{2}$ mile
2. Katie bought a mirror to put in her dollhouse. The perimeter of the mirror is 50 millimeters and the width is 10 millimeters. What is the length?
   15 millimeters
3. Kyle wants to make a fence for his garden. The garden is 24 feet long and 16 feet wide. How much fence does Kyle need to buy?
   80 feet of fence
4. Stella loves to go to the art museum. Her favorite painting is 25 feet wide and 10 feet tall. What is the area of the painting?
   250 feet
5. Mrs. Smith is buying carpet for a small room in her house. She needs 9 square yards. The carpet costs $5 a square yard. How much will Mrs. Smith pay for the carpet?
   $45.00
6. How many square yards of carpet do you need to cover a floor that is 6 yards long and 4 yards wide?
   24 square yards

page 48

Rounding Numbers

Round the numbers to the nearest ten.

248 **250**	63 **60**	71 **70**	326 **330**	104 **100**
97 **100**	56 **60**	1,247 **1,250**	83 **80**	653 **650**
45 **50**	132 **130**	87 **90**	49 **50**	99 **100**
354 **350**	16 **20**	308 **310**	757 **760**	37 **40**

Round the numbers to the nearest hundred.

3,743 **3,700**	12,278 **12,300**	374 **400**	145 **100**
546 **500**	2,453 **2,500**	98 **100**	4,389 **4,400**
2,614 **2,600**	194 **200**	7,643 **7,600**	893 **900**
216 **200**	673 **700**	1,783 **1,800**	574 **600**

Round the numbers to the nearest thousand.

17,524 **18,000**	6,429 **6,000**	3,941 **4,000**	2,642 **3,000**
4,834 **5,000**	4,216 **4,000**	1,823 **2,000**	9,487 **9,000**
23,573 **24,000**	6,840 **7,000**	7,927 **8,000**	1,431 **1,000**
16,743 **17,000**	5,327 **5,000**	9,849 **10,000**	3,347 **3,000**

page 49

Addition Review

Add.

258 + 31 = **289**	368 + 527 = **895**	57 + 36 = **93**	845 + 445 = **1,290**	1,684 + 459 = **2,143**
245 + 124 = **369**	681 + 110 = **791**	1,765 + 4,730 = **6,495**	752 + 774 = **1,526**	26 + 64 = **90**
560 + 230 = **790**	48 + 99 = **147**	3,287 + 1,721 = **5,008**	664 + 201 = **865**	231 + 421 = **652**
76 + 23 = **99**	579 + 457 = **1,036**	7,580 + 1,478 = **9,058**	305 + 185 = **490**	1,400 + 2,624 = **4,024**
309 + 326 = **635**	1,486 + 2,006 = **3,492**	47 + 32 = **79**	6,078 + 1,033 = **7,111**	1,985 + 2,191 = **4,176**

page 50

Multiplication Review I

Multiply.

9 x 7 = **63**	8 x 7 = **56**	6 x 5 = **30**	4 x 3 = **12**	5 x 8 = **40**	6 x 7 = **42**
4 x 7 = **28**	6 x 6 = **36**	5 x 7 = **35**	6 x 3 = **18**	9 x 4 = **36**	8 x 3 = **24**
7 x 7 = **49**	3 x 7 = **21**	9 x 5 = **45**	8 x 8 = **64**	5 x 6 = **30**	7 x 9 = **63**
6 x 6 = **36**	9 x 9 = **81**	5 x 5 = **25**	8 x 4 = **32**	7 x 6 = **42**	3 x 4 = **12**
6 x 9 = **54**	8 x 5 = **40**	5 x 4 = **20**	9 x 7 = **63**	7 x 8 = **56**	8 x 9 = **72**
4 x 6 = **24**	8 x 6 = **48**	9 x 3 = **27**	7 x 4 = **28**	9 x 5 = **45**	3 x 5 = **15**

page 51

Multiplication Review II

Multiply.

12 x 39 = **468**	23 x 7 = **161**	37 x 52 = **1,924**	49 x 4 = **196**	33 x 18 = **594**	22 x 7 = **133**
83 x 8 = **664**	92 x 81 = **7,452**	79 x 8 = **632**	57 x 16 = **912**	85 x 4 = **340**	45 x 17 = **765**
57 x 19 = **1,083**	63 x 3 = **189**	74 x 31 = **2,294**	67 x 6 = **402**	23 x 14 = **322**	24 x 9 = **216**
19 x 7 = **133**	21 x 89 = **1,869**	39 x 5 = **195**	48 x 52 = **2,496**	71 x 7 = **497**	83 x 14 = **1,162**
52 x 27 = **1,404**	18 x 6 = **108**	38 x 29 = **1,102**	47 x 3 = **141**	52 x 13 = **676**	13 x 9 = **117**
41 x 8 = **328**	67 x 18 = **1,206**	79 x 3 = **237**	83 x 19 = **1,577**	93 x 5 = **465**	57 x 12 = **684**

page 52

Multiplication Review III

Multiply.

Remember: Multiply the ones place first. Multiply the tens place second. Then add them together!

613 x 42 = **25,746**	459 x 17 = **7,803**	931 x 31 = **28,861**	372 x 18 = **6,696**	492 x 22 = **10,824**
785 x 73 = **57,305**	412 x 16 = **6,592**	396 x 89 = **35,244**	137 x 45 = **6,165**	209 x 29 = **6,061**
917 x 64 = **58,688**	406 x 92 = **37,352**	381 x 57 = **21,717**	710 x 27 = **19,170**	118 x 72 = **8,496**
814 x 74 = **60,236**	926 x 28 = **25,928**	231 x 13 = **3,003**	174 x 40 = **6,960**	349 x 29 = **10,121**
905 x 81 = **73,305**	714 x 39 = **27,846**	817 x 48 = **39,216**	273 x 12 = **3,276**	384 x 17 = **6,528**

page 53

Division Review I

Divide.

2)4 **2**	9)18 **2**	9)72 **8**	9)0 **0**	6)36 **6**	3)15 **5**	4)20 **5**
7)63 **9**	9)81 **9**	2)14 **7**	5)10 **2**	3)6 **2**	2)2 **1**	7)35 **5**
8)56 **7**	7)49 **7**	5)50 **10**	7)14 **2**	5)25 **5**	2)18 **9**	4)36 **9**
8)72 **9**	4)28 **7**	4)20 **5**	5)30 **6**	9)0 **0**	3)6 **2**	9)81 **9**
9)54 **6**	4)16 **4**	9)63 **7**	5)35 **7**	8)16 **2**	9)45 **5**	5)5 **1**
2)12 **6**	7)14 **2**	6)6 **1**	5)0 **0**	7)49 **7**	8)40 **5**	7)70 **10**
3)12 **4**	9)63 **7**	4)32 **8**	3)21 **7**	8)8 **1**	5)0 **0**	2)14 **7**

page 54

Division Review II

Divide.

7)91 **13**	6)84 **14**	4)97 **24r1**	5)75 **15**	2)82 **41**	3)78 **26**
3)72 **24**	4)68 **17**	5)65 **13**	2)72 **36**	5)70 **14**	7)84 **12**
6)93 **15r3**	7)97 **13r6**	8)96 **12**	3)81 **27**	4)98 **24r2**	8)93 **11r5**
2)98 **49**	4)76 **19**	3)57 **19**	5)92 **18r2**	6)78 **13**	6)72 **12**
2)88 **44**	3)69 **23**	7)91 **13**	6)83 **13r5**	4)94 **23r2**	5)99 **19r4**

page 55

Division Review III

Divide.

8)729 **91r1**	6)375 **62r3**	7)575 **82r1**	9)817 **90r7**	3)472 **157r1**
4)159 **39r3**	8)928 **116**	5)318 **63r3**	7)287 **41**	7)523 **74r5**
3)870 **290**	9)760 **84r4**	6)642 **107**	5)973 **194r3**	9)387 **43**
4)732 **183**	6)849 **141r3**	8)417 **52r1**	7)917 **131**	6)748 **124r4**

page 56

Let Your Brilliance Shine!

1. Write the numbers using Roman Numerals
   66 **LXVI** 47 **XLVII**
2. 4,793 + 349 = **5,142** 3,482 − 684 = **2,798**
3. (4 x 7) − 4 ___ 8 + (6 x 5)
   ○ a. = ● b. < ○ c. = ○ d. >
4. Round the numbers to the nearest thousand.
   7,434 **7,000** 2,921 **3,000** 1,682 **2,000**
5. 4,609.72 − 526.94 = ____
   ○ a. 4,082.73 ○ b. 4,083.78 ● c. 4,082.78 ○ d. 4,183.78
6. 84 ÷ 9 = ____
   ○ a. 850 ○ b. 92 r13 ○ c. 91 r4 ● d. 93 r4
7. Write the standard form of three million, forty six thousand, eight hundred three.
   3,046,803
8. Write the word form for 5,870,403.
   five million, eight hundred seventy thousand, four hundred three
9. Todd's four friends have no sports trading cards of their own. Todd has 246 baseball cards and 134 football cards. He would like to share his cards with his friends. How many cards will Todd and each of his friends receive? Will they all receive the same amount?
   76 cards each
   Yes, they will all receive the same amount.
10. Priscilla and her three friends like to play with dolls at her house. She has quite a collection and always likes to share evenly. Priscilla has 76 dolls. She wants each person to have the same number of dolls. How many will each person get? Will there be any dolls left over?
    19 dolls each
    No, there will not be any dolls left over.
11. Kyle feeds his dog Skippy twice a day. Skippy eats a cup of food each time he is fed. How many cups of food will Skippy eat in a four-week period?
    7x4=28 days 28x2 cups=56 cups

page 57

Show What You Know!

1. Find the missing number in this pattern.
   176, 171, ____, 161, 156
   ○ a. 169 ● b. 166 ○ c. 170 ○ d. 165
2. 187 x 92 = **17,204** 904 x 76 = **68,704**
3. I am > 634. I am even. My digits total 17. What number am I?
   ○ a. 619 ● b. 638 ○ c. 736 ○ d. 566
4. Round the numbers to the nearest hundred.
   3,709 **3,700** 8,324 **8,300** 7,641 **7,600**
5. 132.78 + 8,746.23 = **8,879.01**
6. 9,756 ÷ 8 = **1,219r4**
7. Write the expanded form of 8,746.
   8,000 + 700 + 40 + 6
8. 4 hundreds + 11 tens + 7 ones = ______
   ○ a. 417 ○ b. 418 ● c. 517 ○ d. 507
9. Jill had saved her babysitting money for several months. She has a total of $89.75 and is going to buy a portable CD player for $37.95 and a CD for 15.99. How much money will Jill have left?
   $35.81
10. Chad sells newspapers. He delivered 378 papers on Monday, 264 papers on Tuesday, and 418 papers on Wednesday. About how many papers has Chad delivered so far this week?
    about 1,100
11. Lacey was cleaning her family's closets and found they had a total of 31 pairs of shoes. After talking with the girls at school, she found that Christina's family has 47 pairs of shoes and Emily's small family has 26 pairs of shoes. What method could be used to find how many more pairs of shoes Christina's family has than Emily's family?
    ○ a. Add 31 and 26. ○ b. Subtract 31 from 47.
    ○ c. Add 26 and 31 and subtract the sum from 47. ● d. Subtract 26 from 47.

page 58

Fractions and Decimals

Numbers less than a whole can be written two ways—as a fraction or as a decimal. Rewrite the numbers as fractions or decimals.

$\frac{2}{10}$ = **.2**	$\frac{40}{100}$ **.40**	$\frac{8}{10}$ = **.8**
.9 = **$\frac{9}{10}$**	.46 = **$\frac{46}{100}$**	.79 = **$\frac{79}{100}$**
$\frac{53}{100}$ = **.53**	$\frac{3}{10}$ **.3**	$\frac{31}{100}$ = **.31**
.56 = **$\frac{56}{100}$**	.7 = **$\frac{7}{10}$**	.5 = **$\frac{5}{10}$**
$\frac{6}{10}$ = **.6**	$\frac{28}{100}$ **.28**	$\frac{1}{10}$ = **.1**
.83 = **$\frac{83}{100}$**	.98 = **$\frac{98}{100}$**	.4 = **$\frac{4}{10}$**
$\frac{62}{100}$ = **.62**	.92 = **$\frac{92}{100}$**	$\frac{43}{100}$ = **.43**
$\frac{7}{10}$ = **.7**	.37 = **$\frac{37}{100}$**	$\frac{18}{100}$ = **.18**
.51 = **$\frac{51}{100}$**	$\frac{27}{100}$ = **.27**	.82 = **$\frac{82}{100}$**
$\frac{3}{10}$ = **.3**	.8 = **$\frac{8}{10}$**	$\frac{19}{100}$ = **.19**
.21 = **$\frac{21}{100}$**	$\frac{79}{100}$ = **.79**	.13 = **$\frac{13}{10}$**
$\frac{63}{100}$ = **.63**	.43 = **$\frac{43}{100}$**	$\frac{74}{100}$ = **.74**

page 59

Mixed Review I

1. Which is the most likely to have the capacity of a gallon?
   ○ a. kitchen sink ● b. water jug ○ c. bath tub ○ d. soda can
2. A bathtub would have the capacity of:
   ○ a. 3 gallons ○ b. 4 pints ● c. 50 liters ○ d. 1 cup
3. Grandma was in the baking mood. She decided to make a cake for each of her five grandchildren. Each cake called for eight ounces of cocoa. How many ounces of cocoa did grandma have to buy?
   40 ounces
4. Bill needs his morning coffee. If his coffee pot holds one quart of coffee and he pours himself one cup. How much is in the pot now?
   3 cups
5. An elephant would be measured in what?
   ○ a. pounds ● b. tons ○ c. millimeters ○ d. gallons
6. An encyclopedia would be weighed in what?
   ○ a. grams ● b. kilograms
   If one encyclopedia weighed 2 **kg**, how much would 8 weigh? **16 kg**
7. Tim has a bag of marbles that weighs 18 grams. If Jeff's bag of marbles weighs 27 grams, how much more does Jeff's bag weigh than Tim's?
   9 grams
8. If a new born baby weighs 7 lbs., how many ounces is that?
   112 ounces
9. Lacey and Tim competed in a dance marathon. They danced for a total of 4 hours and 28 minutes. How many **minutes** did Lacey and Tim dance?
   ○ a. 240 min. ○ b. 258 min. ○ c. 158 min. ● d. 268 min.
10. Beth checked out a new book from the library. She just couldn't put it down. She read for a total of 1 hour and 57 minutes yesterday and finished it today by reading for 48 minutes. How many total hours and minutes did it take her to read the book?
    2 hours and 45 minutes

page 60

Mixed Review II

Solve the problems.

1. Round 564 to the nearest ten.
   ○ a. 570 ○ b. 565 ● c. 560 ○ d. 600
2. Round 5,758 to the nearest hundred.
   ○ a. 6,000 ● b. 5,800 ○ c. 5,760 ○ d. 5,700
3. Alora bought eight hair ribbons. Each ribbon was 18 inches long. How many yards of ribbon did Alora purchase?
   ○ a. 8 yds. 9 in. ○ b. 9 yds. ○ c. 11 yds. 10 in. ● d. 4 yds.
4. The circus ran out of pennies and nickels to make change so it had to round everything to the nearest $0.10. What will a $0.78 item cost?
   ○ a. $0.75 ● b. $0.80 ○ c. $1.00 ○ d. $0.70
5. 578 x 27 = **15,606** 693 x 48 = **33,264**
6. 278 ÷ 4 = **69r2** 3,764 ÷ 8 = **470r4**
7. How much of the pizza has been eaten? Simplify your fraction.
   $\frac{2}{8} = \frac{1}{4}$

   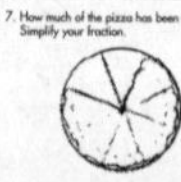
8. Karen is older than David. Mark is older than Karen. Angie is older Mark. Who is the oldest?
   Angie
9. Connie has a doctor's appointment at 3:30 p.m. She was held up at school and didn't arrive until 4:50 p.m. How late was Connie?
   1 hour and 20 minutes
10. Find the greatest common factor for each fraction and simplify.
    $\frac{16}{64}$ = **$\frac{1}{4}$** $\frac{9}{54}$ = **$\frac{1}{6}$** $\frac{25}{40}$ = **$\frac{5}{8}$**